CREATION STILL GOES ON

F. L. BOSCHKE

CREATION STILL GOES ON

Translated from the German
by
L. PARKS

McGRAW-HILL BOOK COMPANY
NEW YORK   TORONTO   LONDON

PREFACE

THE apparently stable picture of the universe given in many generations of school textbooks has recently grown rather blurred. The steady stream of discoveries and new ideas never dries up, and ever bolder theories and forecasts are propounded. Vast amounts of capital and labour are poured into research. It is not always the expert in his field who achieves the most spectacular success, but the age of chance discoveries is definitely over. Today, more than ever in the past, the scientific worker needs specialist knowledge in more fields than one. Astronomy, physics, chemistry, geology and biology have become inter-linked, and are applied jointly to the practical solution of problems which in the past could be tackled only on the basis of speculative assumptions. Cosmology and probing into the origin of life are no longer purely academic subjects. They are closely connected with industrial and economic problems and, last but not least, with military and economic considerations. Fierce rivalry prevails among scientists. The men on the research front are not less exposed to criticism than financiers or industrialists. The scientist's responsibility is not smaller than that of the statesman who makes use, either peaceful or dangerous, of his inventions.

No wonder scientists use cautious phrases, such as "We believe it possible to assume that . . .", when they make their pronouncements, for instance, at the meetings of Nobel Prize winners at Lindau on Lake Constance. Their communications are of such immeasurable consequence, and are so alien to our accepted views of the world, that we have almost given up trying to harmonise them with our own ideas and to visualise the possible practical effects of all their novelties. As far as science is concerned, we have become believers in miracles. We accept scientific statements without understanding them, and the time seems near when the belief in science will have outpaced all other kinds of belief.

The ability to doubt has disappeared, and with it the capacity for wonder. That is a pity, because the natural sciences have opened a window to a wider universe than we have ever known. We have to reconcile ourselves to the idea

v

that our world is not unique. This is a subject for marvel, even more than for belief and understanding.

Everything we now know conflicts with the idea that our tiny earth is a privileged place in the universe, and there is no evidence that man is the highest creature in creation. Whatever happened on our planet in the "seven days of creation" as described in the Book of Genesis may also have occurred in the past, or may be occurring now, in a very similar way, on other celestial bodies. The quintessence of all research in cosmic space is that creation has not yet been completed. The genesis of the universe continues, but it is taking place on a larger time-scale than the genesis of our earth.

The chroniclers who wrote the story of the creation in about 600 B.C. were naturally unable to express time in any other way than in days and years. They recorded that the world was created in seven days. The contradiction between the Holy Scriptures and the knowledge of scientists, who attribute a period of millions of years to the development of the earth from its initial formation to the appearance on it of a living cell, is only an apparent one. The seven days may simply represent the seven stages of development of an inhabited planet. The Book of Genesis expresses in the simplest and most comprehensible way the extremely complicated process of evolution which took place before any human witnesses were present.

What have scientists discovered about the actual events of the first "seven days"? Was there a "beginning", or is "the beginning", like "eternity", outside time and its measurable progression?

This book was designed to give answers to these questions. We are still merely at the beginning of our knowledge of the origin of life. However, the little we know, or can at least assume with some degree of confidence, shows us an overwhelming picture of what has happened and what is still happening. Over a number of years we have gained much knowledge about the origin of our neighbouring planets, and it lies within the bounds of possibility that further progress in space research will soon depend merely on the "living conditions" on other celestial bodies.

The exploration of the history of the creation of heaven and earth takes us through all fields of science. Many theories and hypotheses, however, meet repeatedly at certain points, and therefore we shall attempt to take the most direct route. The last few years have been so rich in scientific discoveries that many traditional, allegedly proven assertions have been superseded and deserve to be remembered merely for the boldness of their conception. Sober laboratory analysis has confounded many elaborate edifices constructed by imaginative thinkers. Research, and a life devoted to research, are nevertheless full of adventure, and a book which attempts to give an answer to the question of the origin of life may, nay must, on occasion be adventurous too.

F. L. B.

Heidelberg
January 1962

CONTENTS

ix

III

Let the waters under the heaven be gathered together
unto one place and let the dry land appear

IV

Let the earth bring forth the living creature after his kind

ILLUSTRATIONS IN COLOUR

SOURCES

1. Dr. G. Lange-Hesse, Max Planck Institute of Aeronomy
2. Zentrale Farbbild Agentur, Heidelberg
3. Carl J. Shipek, San Diego, U.S.A.
4. E. Krug, Berlin
5. Amerika-Dienst, Bad Godesberg

PHOTOGRAPHS

xv

SOURCES

1. Professor Willard F. Libby, University of California, Los Angeles
2. Fabian Bachrach
3. Professor Herr, Max Planck Institute for Chemistry, Mainz
4. Binz
5. Professor Hentschel, Geologisches Landesamt, Wiesbaden
6. John S. Shelton, Claremont, California
7. Picture archive of the Deutsches Museum, Munich
8. Aluminium-Zentrale, Düsseldorf
9. Stanford Research Institute, California
10. Lawrence Radiation Laboratory, Berkeley, California
11. W. Stuhler
12. Picture Archive of the Süddeutsche Zeitung, Munich
13. Professor Hans Pettersson, Oceanographic Institute, Göteborg
14. Angewandte Chemie, Heidelberg
15. California Institute of Technology
16. Press Unit of the American Embassy, Bad Godesberg
17. Dr. Heinz Dombrowski, Bad Nauheim
18. Triangel-Sandoz-Zeitschrift für medizinische Wissenschaft
19. Associated Press, Frankfurt/Main
20. Press Department of the U.S.S.R. Embassy, Bonn
21. Historisches Bildarchiv Handke, Bad Berneck

DIAGRAMS AND ILLUSTRATIONS IN THE TEXT

SOURCES

1. Deutsches Museum, Munich
2. Proceedings of the U.S.S.R. Academy of Sciences, Moscow, 1960
3. Cord-Christian Troebst, *Der Griff nach dem Mond*, published by Econ-Verlag, Düsseldorf, 1959
4. Historia-Photo, Bad Sachsa

The author and the publishers thank the scientists and the scientific establishments, as well as others, for the supply of illustrations and the permission to reproduce them.

I

In the beginning God created the heaven and the earth
Genesis I. 1

The question that springs to mind when we read the first words of the Bible is: When was that beginning?

Until the middle of this century all ideas and methods of determining the beginning of time proved unsatisfactory. Today new methods allow us accurately to measure the age of various organic and inorganic substances. These allow us to explore not only the age during which the story of Genesis originated, but periods even more remote. With the help of the isotope clock we are groping slowly back through the ages until we finally realise that the earth, and the universe itself, are of limited age.

CHAPTER 1

THE ISOTOPE CLOCK

*Libby corrects the historians. Radioactivity from above.
Ancient exhaust gases. The world clock acquires a minute
hand.*

WHEN did it happen? That is the standard question of detectives, research historians, biologists and astronomers. We, too, ask this question of ourselves and others daily, and so frequently, that we are no longer conscious of it.

When did it happen? To answer this question science has evolved a method which makes juggling with dates impossible. This is called isotope dating, and its "clockwork" is radioactive decay. We know of no way of influencing the working of this "clock". No matter whether a substance is exposed to maximum temperatures or to extreme pressures, and regardless of whatever else is done with it, the decay rate of its radioactive components does not change; and there is hardly any substance without at least some trace of radioactivity.

The officials of the Department of Egyptology of the Chicago Natural History Museum could scarcely believe their ears when one day they received the startling request to open the glass case containing the funerary boat of King Sesostris III of Egypt, and to cut from its deck planks a 12 inch square. This was sacrilege! The Egyptologists' indignation would have been greater still had they known of the intended fate of their precious piece of timber.

Professor Willard F. Libby of the Department of Chemistry, University of California in Los Angeles, a renowned radiochemist and a long-standing member of the United States Atomic Energy Commission, intended to split this wood into chips and burn it to charcoal in the electrical furnace of his laboratory. He had no interest in the piece of timber as a sample of Egyptian craftsmanship, he was merely concerned with obtaining wood which was not only ancient, but the exact age of which was known. The historians were agreed that the funerary boat had been built 3,750 years ago.

Charcoal, the substance Libby wanted to obtain, is almost

21

pure carbon, a chemical element the atomic weight of which is almost exactly 12, i.e., a carbon atom is roughly twelve times heavier than the lightest known atom, that of hydrogen. To be precise, however, not all carbon atoms are as light as 12, there are carbon atoms whose weight is not 12 but 14. This variant of a pure element is called an isotope. The chemical symbol for carbon is "C", and, in order to refer to the isotope in question, chemists place the weight figure in front of the letter and write "^{12}C" or "^{14}C".

The uranium isotope with a weight of 235, i.e., ^{235}U, has become famous, or infamous, as the basic uranium isotope required for the generation of atomic energy. We know that this isotope splits occasionally, but we still do not know why it does so. However, in order to sketch at least an approximate picture of the process, we could perhaps assume that the isotope suffers from a kind of disease. Some ^{235}U atoms are "dying off" all the time, and in this way other and new elements originate. If these ^{235}U isotopes "live" very close to each other they can "infect" each other. Their decay products (neutrons) impinge on neighbouring ^{235}U isotopes, infect them, and cause them, too, to die and, in turn, infect their neighbours. We even know the rate at which the ^{235}U isotopes die off: after every 710 million years half of them are dead, i.e., split, decayed. In this way we get a picture of the process which physicists call "chain reaction".

Carbon decay processes are similar: ^{12}C is "healthy", but ^{14}C decays. However, its decay is not "infectious", for it emits only electrons, negative electrical charge units, or so-called beta rays. If we had an ounce of ^{14}C, only half an ounce would be left after 5,560 years, only a quarter of an ounce after double that time, i.e., 11,120 years, and so on. This ^{14}C isotope is of extra-terrestrial origin, for it originates in a nuclear chemical reaction about 19 miles above the earth, under the influence of cosmic rays from space.

Nuclear physicists formulate this reaction as:

$$^{14}N \ (n,p) \ ^{14}C$$

which means that when a nitrogen isotope with a mass of 14 (^{14}N) collides with a neutron, a proton ("p"—a positively charged component of an atomic nucleus) is released from the nitrogen, and carbon-14 (^{14}C) is generated. Experiments in an atomic reactor have proved that this formula is correct.

From the "beginning of time" we have been receiving ^{14}C continuously and fairly regularly from the atmosphere. At the same time, ^{14}C has been decaying continuously at the above-mentioned rate of one-half in 5,560 years. A balance between ^{14}C formation and ^{14}C decay has come to pass long ago. Carbon is contained in plants which, in order to build their cells, absorb it from the air in the form of carbon dioxide (CO_2). Plants are eaten by animals and by men, and therefore the established carbon-12–14 ratio is found throughout the whole of living nature.

However, when plants or animals die, they cease to absorb carbon-14, and the content of the latter decreases in the vegetable or animal remains in accordance with the law of radioactive decay.

The timber of the Egyptian funerary boat was 3,750 years old, and so its ^{14}C content had been decreasing for 3,750 years. The question was whether Libby would be able to find the remaining ^{14}C content in the timber, and, what is more, determine it with the necessary degree of precision.

Of every half ounce of carbon in a live organism, roughly 200 carbon-14 atoms decay every minute. Therefore, Libby's measuring instruments had to be capable of determining fewer than, say, 150 atom decays per half ounce of carbon per minute. Of course, a sample of more than half an ounce could have been used for the experiment, but in 1944 the accurate measurement of this rate of decay in even two ounces was a considerable achievement. The natural radioactivity of the laboratory walls and even the faint natural radiation of the physicists' bodies, had to be eliminated. The sensitive instruments were built into protective iron blocks. Even then the penetrating high-energy particles of cosmic rays which manage to reach the surface of the earth could have interfered with the accuracy of measurement. Therefore Libby and his colleagues surrounded their measuring instrument, a Geiger–Müller counter, with other counters which switched off the recording device every time a cosmic particle penetrated the measuring installation. This experiment was designed to provide a proof which could not be gainsaid. The experiment succeeded. The measured residual amount of carbon-14 in the timber of the funerary boat yielded the age of 3,621 years. Being careful by nature, Libby allowed the possibility of a maximum margin of error of 180 years either way. But what did that matter? The value of the method of determining the age of organic substances by means of their carbon-14 content had been proved. Now we are able to determine when an organism died; when an ancient tree of which we find relics was cut down; when the flax of which an ancient piece of cloth was made was dried; and when an animal or man whose remains have been excavated perished. The hour hand of our world clock had been discovered by physics and proved correct.

Libby corrects the historians

Charcoal found in the temple city of Monte Alban in Mexico was dated by the new method and determined to be 2,600 years old. In a cave buried by volcanic action in Oregon 300 pairs of ancient sandals were discovered, tidily stacked. They were among the oldest human artefacts found in the United States, a prehistoric shoe store 9,035 years old, according to Libby's carbon clock.

In Nebraska there are places where the so-called Lime Creek Man is said to have lived. Historians had estimated the charcoal of his fires to be 20,000, or perhaps even 30,000 years old. They were wrong, said Professor Libby, for these remains are only 9,520 years old, possibly 450 years older than that, but not older than 10,000 years.

In many cases Libby was able to correct the estimates of the historians and give the exact age of things. Stems and roots of water weeds from the Texepan-Man period found in Mexico had been estimated at 10,000 years, but they were shown to be only 4,100 years old. On the southern outskirts of Mexico City there stands the Toltec pyramid of Cuicuilco, which had been partially buried by a lava stream. Geologists were asked about the age of the pyramid. They estimated the age of the lava deposit at 8,000 years. That would have made Toltec culture older than any Occidental civilisation. Libby succeeded in obtaining some charcoal from a layer below the lava, and he gave its age as a mere 2,400 years. Remains of timber were found in the famous Lascaux cave in southern France, and French scientists estimated its age as 50,000 years, while other palaeontologists would admit to only 10,000 or 20,000 years. Libby settled their argument; his carbon-atom clock indicated 15,500 years.

However, it is not only timber whose carbon content can yield a definite result by the application of this method. A piece

24

of beeswax from Britain, believed to be 2,500–3,000 years old, was proved to be much younger, only 820 years old. Snail shells were excavated in an ancient Mesopotamian settlement, and Libby established their age as 6,700 years. A large dam consisting of thousands of wooden stakes was found near Boston, U.S.A. Its construction was very similar to the contemporary fish dams in the Hudson River near New York, but the Boston dam proved to be about 5,000 years old. The Hawaiian Islands were shown to have been inhabited for a mere 1,000 years.

On Salisbury Plain near the ancient highway from London to Bristol the mysterious stones of Stonehenge form a circle about 270 feet in diameter. The huge angular stone blocks rise to a height of 13 feet, and some are as much as 7 feet wide. More rocks are placed inside the circle. Who were the people who dragged the 50-ton blocks about 150 miles from the nearest spot where they could have originated? How did they achieve this technical feat, an imitation of which would cause us some headaches even today? We do not know. The people are believed to have been Celts, who may have practised some kind of sun worship there. Ancient charcoal was found at Stonehenge, and now we know definitely that people were there 3,800 years ago, but we do not know whether they were the builders of Stonehenge, workmen who lit a camp fire, or priests who celebrated a sacrifice.

The survey of carbon dating examples could be expanded almost indefinitely. One of the oldest items which has been successfully dated recently was the Alpine palaeolithic find in the Salzofen cave near Bad Aussee, Austria, where charcoal from a bone layer was dated as being 32,050 ($\pm$ 3,000) years old.

The decisive success of the new dating method, which has been improved considerably since 1947 in regard to the required amount of carbon, as well as the accuracy of the instruments, was, however, achieved in another field. We have all heard of ancient calendars of extinct peoples who listed the reigns of their kings, the building of their palaces, and their wars, by their own reckoning of time, unrelated to our present Christian calendar. The carbon-14 method made it possible to compare the calendars and their system of counting the years, and to correlate them. The successful dating of the Babylonian calendar of Hammurabi's era made it possible to discard all but one of the various proposed correlations between the Babylonian and Christian calendars.

Some dating was possible even in regard to the earth's history. In favourable cases the carbon clock can measure the past as far back as 70,000 years. In 1953 Libby succeeded in reaching back to the Ice Age by determining the age of the remains of trees and lumps of peat from a North American bog which was known to have originated during the most recent local Ice Age. This had been assumed to have been about 25,000 years before our era, but Libby established from several analyses made with his carbon clock an average figure of only 11,400 years. Since then the various Ice Ages for the whole of North America have been accurately dated at numerous locations.

About 10,400 B.C. the last great glacier melting took place, and it is assumed that North America became inhabited by man soon after that. The charcoal remains of the oldest discovered fires date from that period.

Beneath the deserts of Egypt there are vast water resources. It was not known whether they consisted of seepage water which collected far below from the surrounding countryside, or whether they were the residue from the Ice Age which resulted in heavy rainfall in those regions. If the water was due to seepage, digging wells would be profitable even if they turned out to be very expensive, for desert lands could then be irrigated. These questions were solved by a study group from Heidelberg with surprising results. By testing water samples with the ^{14}C isotope clock for carbon content, it was discovered that the water was old. Additional wells would only result in exhausting this ancient reservoir the sooner. However, near the Nile and the sea-coast the ground water was of recent date, i.e., the result of rainfall.

Radioactivity from above

Some peculiar phenomena were observed during the years of research on the carbon clock and on the improvement of measuring methods.

On July 16th, 1945, the first, small, experimental atomic bomb was exploded near Alamagordo in the New Mexican desert. Straw cartons manufactured barely three weeks later at a paper mill over a thousand miles away were bought by the Eastman Kodak Co. for packing X-ray films. After another fortnight the firm began to get complaints that the X-ray films were useless because, on development, they were found to be covered with large foggy patches. The returned films were tested. There had been no fault in the manufacture, so the fault must be due to the packaging. It turned out that the cartons had caused the trouble, for they contained fine radioactive particles which "exposed" the film by their radiation. The dust of the atomic bomb had been blown by the wind into the river, the water of which was used by the paper mill.

This incident was the first indication of the dangers of radioactive contamination.

Soon afterwards the firm of E. I. Du Pont requested all its suppliers of materials used for photochemical production to test them for artificial radioactivity before delivery.

In 1951 radioactive snow fell in Washington, D.C., in Rochester, N.Y., and in Detroit. During the summer of 1952 the radiation from radioactive rain in Chicago reached a level which gave rise to anxiety. Paris was the first place in Europe to report radioactive precipitates. On October 18th, 1951, a radioactive dust cloud which twelve days earlier had been over the United States was recorded in Freiburg im Breisgau in Western Germany.

Mankind began to realise the danger. More and more radioactive material was precipitated from the atmosphere. Every year the reports became more alarming, and even today we do not know the extent of the danger of radioactive fall-out.

The dust of all atomic-bomb explosions contains considerable quantities of carbon-14. Every sample of a substance whose age is to be determined now contains additional carbon-14. The natural balance has been upset. The ratio has veered away from ^{12}C towards ^{14}C, and we now measure a ^{14}C value which makes the sample appear less old than it actually is. In order to avoid mistakes, three kinds of carbon material have now to be distinguished: (1) material which contains additional atomic-bomb carbon-14; (2) "normal" carbon samples from plants or minerals whose carbon content is pre-1945; and (3) "very ancient carbon", in the form of coal or oil, both of which are so old that all carbon-14 which they contained decayed long ago. The amount of atomic-bomb carbon-14 on earth now is no longer assessable. Between March, 1955, and March, 1958, the carbon content in the troposphere of the northern hemisphere is assumed to have increased by 5 per cent a year. Since then large quantities have been added by Russian atomic-bomb tests. When, or rather how soon, these quantities will drop down to the earth's surface is conjectural: estimates vary between four

27

and fifteen years. If no further bombs are exploded the excessive ^{14}C value will decrease again after its half-life period; i.e., after roughly 5,600 years our descendants will have only half our troubles.

Ancient exhaust gases

The increase of ^{14}C is not the only difficulty which the carbon-14 method has to face as a result of modern technical developments.

The Heidelberg Institute of Physics has an up-to-date installation for carbon dating by Libby's method. In 1955 some of its students and research assistants followed up a casual suggestion by going to the neighbouring arterial motor road and picking some leafy branches from the wayside trees. The carbon clock came up with the fantastic answer that these branches were 500 years old.

The testers' suspicions were thus confirmed: on the one hand, fall-out falsified carbon-14 dating results by making things appear younger than they were, and, on the other hand, another and opposite effect had now been discovered which simulated excessive age values. The explanation is that car engines burn oil products, and oil originated during an early age of the earth's history, and therefore no longer contains carbon-14. The exhaust gases consequently contain no ^{14}C, and the carbon content of the carbon dioxide component of the air, which the plants growing along the motor road used to build their branches and leaves, had become diluted to an extent which made the air appear 500 years old. If this is what happens to the air around a country motor road, what about a town centre? Tests showed that all growing things in towns were affected by exhaust gases in exactly the same way, and they, too, reacted to the test as if they were 500 years old.

It is not only the motor exhaust gases that interfere with the natural ^{14}C balance. The improved sensitivity of measuring methods soon showed that our customary heating installations have also made their contribution to this state of affairs. Coal, coke and oil fuel release carbon dioxide lacking the ^{14}C component, and thus they dilute the natural ^{14}C radioactivity in the air. According to measurements made in 1902, the carbon dioxide content of the air was 0·029 per cent; today it is 0·032 per cent.

The carbon-14 content of the atmosphere, which steadily

decreased in the ninety years of industrialisation after 1870, is now being more than balanced out again through nuclear explosions. Is that a welcome restoration of the natural balance? Definitely not. But future generations of physicists will certainly find this an interesting field of research.

The carbon clock begins to run down inexorably in an organism as soon as death occurs, and its "tick" becomes gradually quieter and weaker. After 5,560 years only half its strength remains, after 11,120 years only a quarter and after 22,240 years only one-sixteenth of the original carbon-14 activity is to be expected, i.e., roughly only 25 atomic decays per ounce of carbon per minute. The instruments with which carbon-14 traces can be detected in favourable circumstances in animal and plant remains up to 70,000 years old are masterly achievements. Beyond that limit the clock no longer works. It also fails to work with recently living samples, irrespective of the errors caused by nuclear explosions and exhaust gases, for the very small rate of carbon-14 losses in the first decades after death affects the accuracy of measurement. For a reasonable degree of accuracy samples should be at least 400 years old. That is the irritating handicap of the carbon-14 dating method.

What can be done about it? We have found an hour hand for the atomic clock, and it should be possible to find a minute hand, too.

The world clock acquires a minute hand

Professor Libby and his colleagues pondered this problem. They needed some substance that was naturally abundant, was continuously generated anew and had the property of radioactive decay. Libby fell back on cosmic-ray reactions. A reaction of possible interest takes place in the highest layers of the earth's atmosphere; the nitrogen there, in Libby's opinion, should form tritium with the neutrons from cosmic rays. He formulated the reaction as:

$$^{14}N + 1 \text{ neutron} \longrightarrow {}^{12}C + T \text{ (tritium)}$$

Tritium, however, is an isotope of hydrogen, which is a chemical component of water, and water abounds on earth. The essential point for the experiment was that tritium is radioactive; it decays by half in $12\frac{1}{2}$ years.

The scientists were doubtful about the possibility of using

tritium. When they examined the possibilities of the carbon clock they tried to calculate the total volume of carbon-14 on earth. They discovered that on every square inch of our globe 15 carbon-14 atoms decayed per second. Therefore there should be a total of about 80 tons of ^{14}C on earth.

But what about tritium? Tritium should come down to earth from the upper atmosphere with rain, but what was the total rainfall on earth, and how much of it contained tritium? Research into these problems produced surprising answers. The tritium content of rain varies. In summer, rain in the Chicago region was found to contain only half the amount of tritium it contained in winter. The reason is that in summer the rain clouds come from the Gulf of Mexico, i.e., consist of water that has evaporated there. In winter, rain and snow are mostly brought by the wind from the Pacific, across the whole American continent. The summer rain clouds travel a comparatively short distance, and therefore have little time to take up tritium from the atmosphere. The journey from the Pacific is much longer, and therefore more tritium is collected. On the other hand, the distance from the Pacific is not so great that the tritium has time to decay to any considerable extent.

When Libby and his colleagues made a few calculations they came to the depressing conclusion that the total amount of natural tritium on earth was scarcely more than 55 oz, just over 3 lb, of which about one-third of an ounce was in the atmosphere.

Professor Libby wondered how he could prove the suitability of tritium for age determination. If only he could obtain some "ancient" water! He could hardly hope that some pilgrim somewhere had devoutly preserved large quantities of holy water, and in any case he would have to know where the water came from and the date on which it was collected. All his attempts to get a sufficiently large quantity of authentic "old" water were unsuccessful, as was only to be expected, and he seemed to have reached a dead end.

Then he had a flash of inspiration. There was plenty of old water for sale under the trade name of "wine". In the eyes of a physicist, wine is no more than old rain water, admittedly full of impurities, such as alcohol, aromatic substances and a few salts, but substantially just old water. Even the other requisite condition was present; the labels on the bottles not only stated the year when the water was collected and the place of its origin, but even more exact information, such as "late harvest", etc., was often also provided.

Libby started ordering the oldest wines from all over the world, from the Moselle, from California, from Portugal; he even ordered a large consignment of well-matured Scotch whisky. Then he proceeded to empty the bottles and to distil the useless alcohol away. The quality of the "water" did not count, only the exact information about its place of origin and age.

This experiment was successful. His measuring instruments usually produced the same answer as the label. When it differed, the label was a lie. Very soon no one could sell him a young wine for an old one. Tritium dating research began in earnest. Was the water in a spring recent rain water, or had it spent scores of years in the lower layers of the earth's crust? If it was rain water the tritium content was high. Libby was able to demonstrate that the stream water of Lardarelle in Italy was old, and so was that from the well of the McDonald Observatory in Texas. Contrary to all expectations, the hot spring water at Hot Springs, Arkansas, turned out to be rain water. Samples from the glaciers of Greenland to which the tritium dating method was applied showed the age of the various layers of ice.

Libby's carbon-14 dating method determines age over a range of 70,000 years. All we have unearthed in the way of remains of human civilisation comes within that period. Our step into the past, even if it is small, has taken us nearer to the days of creation.

For his work Libby was awarded the highest scientific award. Although he is in the first place a physicist, he received the Nobel Prize for Chemistry in 1960.

CHAPTER 2

HOW OLD IS THE EARTH?

*The futility of duplicated work. The Drachenfels is still
young. From what moment can our planet be called "Earth"?*

THE measuring instruments and counters of radioactive decay
are now working away in laboratories all over the world, and
museums too have recognised the value of the new dating
methods. Our world clock has now not only hour hands but
also minute hands which have become indispensable for research. Mere speculation about the date of origin of some
archaeological find, or about the genuineness or possible subsequent falsification of an historical document, is now futile.

However, a measurement range of 70,000 years is negligible
compared with the terrestrial age of millions of years, and we
are still a long way away from the answer to the question of how
old the earth is.

When the Irish Bishop James Ussher stated in 1654 that the
world was created at 9 a.m. on October 26th, 4004 B.C., the
information was explicit and precise, and one is bound to
acknowledge that the cleric had devoted much diligence to the
study of the Bible to reach such a precise conclusion. However,
that does not make his calculations reliable.

More trust, perhaps, can be placed in the modest claims of
the French physicist Dominique François Arago, who in 1837
investigated the heat losses of the earth. His starting-point was
the notion that the earth was originally an incandescent
celestial body. By measuring the rate of its gradual heat loss it
should, in his opinion, be possible to calculate reasonably
accurately how many centuries had elapsed since it was red hot.
As a scientist Arago was aware of the limitations of this method,
and expressed himself cautiously:

> "The solution of the much discussed problem of the age of
> our earth, including the period of its incandescent state, rests
> on the observation of a temperature difference, the minute-
> ness of which is undiscernible by our present methods, and
> will therefore have to be left to future centuries."

Professor Libby's carbon dating equipment. On the left, recording instruments. On the right, with the shutter open, the shielded counter array: the main measuring counter in the centre, surrounded by eleven subsidiary counters

Professor Willard F. Libby of California University, Los Angeles

A sandal found in Eastern Oregon, 9,035 (±325) years old, according to Libby's carbon dating method

Linen wrapping of the Dead Sea scrolls (Book of Isaiah) 1,917 (±200) years old, according to Libby

Later, however, he plucked up courage, and in a subsequent chapter asserted that at any rate in the past two thousand years "the temperature of the earth has, generally speaking, not changed by as much as a tenth of a degree", a claim which is unfortunately now open to doubt.

Many other theorists have assumed, like Arago, that the earth started its existence in a molten state. Today a large number of scientists vehemently deny this. Others postulate a cold period of formation, followed by heating to very high temperatures.

It is obvious that a continuous rate of decrease in the heat of the earth cannot be used as a criterion for determining its age. Perhaps the now thoroughly explored method of utilising the decrease in radioactivity could be used instead.

The futility of duplicated work

Important scientific discoveries are frequently not recognised as such at first. Another phenomenon frequently encountered in the history of science is the simultaneous work of two scientists on the same problem, unknown to one another.

Such a coincidence occurred in 1912. In the already famous Vienna Radium Institute, Stefan Meyer gave his student Fritz A. Paneth the task of isolating the so-called "radium D" from pitchblende, the uranium mineral, by separating it chemically from ordinary lead. Paneth, a young Viennese, whose father was a well-known scientist, and who was destined to have a brilliant career as well as to experience the hard fate of an exile, started work on the task, assuming that it would not prove too difficult.

In 1911 similar problems were exercising the minds of scientists at Manchester University. Professor Ernest Rutherford, the Nobel Prize winner, received in his laboratory a guest research worker whose fame later equalled his own. The young scientist was Georg von Hevesy, and, unaware of the work in progress in Vienna, Rutherford gave his temporary assistant almost the same task as that given to Paneth in Vienna.

The efforts of both young scientists were unsuccessful.

Shortly afterwards Paneth and von Hevesy met by chance in Vienna. Both were convinced by their numerous failures that it was impossible to separate radium D from lead. While they discussed the problem, they suddenly realised the startling fact that radium D did not differ chemically from lead, and therefore could not be separated from it by chemical means. However, radium D was radioactive, and by the emission of radiation changed into other types of lead (lead isotopes). Furthermore, if radioactive lead was added to one of several pieces of lead, the piece to which the addition was made was physically distinctive, but chemically indistinguishable from the other pieces. Even if all the bits of lead were individually dissolved in acids, the solution of the sample which contained the radioactive lead could still be identified. The radiation of the lead isotope served as the indicator.

Paneth was aged twenty-five years and von Hevesy barely twenty-eight. The concept of isotopes was then unknown, and knowledge of radioactivity was still in its infancy, but during their meeting in Vienna these two young men laid the foundations of the isotope-labelling techniques of today, without which we cannot imagine modern biology, chemistry, geology, physics, dietetics or medicine. In the past few years these atomic labelling methods have spread to all branches of industry. They simplify many investigations and annually save industry millions. Since we now have nuclear reactors at our disposal, there are few elements of which no radioactive isotopes are obtainable. A new branch of industry has developed and today delivers hundreds, and even thousands, of labelled products for all types of special purposes. Isotopes are used to test the wear of tyres, to ensure leak-proof oil pipelines, to monitor the passage of a drug to the part of the body for which it is intended, to study the life cycle of a butterfly and a multitude of other things. Everywhere isotopes reduce the required effort to a minimum. Radioactive isotopes of carbon, phosphorus, iodine and many other elements, as well as radium D lead are now in use.

In 1913 Paneth's and von Hevesy's fundamental discoveries were recorded in the proceedings of the meetings of the Imperial Academy of Sciences in Vienna under the title "Radioactive Elements as Indicators in Analytical Chemistry".

The Drachenfels is still young

Again we ask, can these techniques be used in determining the age of the earth?

Let us take an example. Suppose we have a fragment of white rock and wish to know its age. A geologist should know, but he shrugs his shoulders, and suggests that it is chalk formed from shells of marine animals and belongs to the Triassic age, so named from the "trio" of strata: mottled sandstone, marl and keuper. Marl is the name given to the layer consisting largely of mollusc and snail shells and similar deposits. We now know enough for a start. This layer consists of animal remains, therefore it originated long after the formation of the earth. Mottled sandstone is slightly older than marl, according to the geologist, and we are prepared to accept what he says. Even a superficial observation shows that the reddish sandstone consists merely of compressed grains of sand. Now we want to know where the sand came from, and ultimately get right down to bedrock.

There is no method of searching for the oldest type of rock other than that evolved from Paneth's and von Hevesy's researches. The formerly mysterious radium D is only one of the decay products of the type of uranium called ^{238}U. A piece of pitchblende, the uranium mineral, contains all the decay products which, in the course of time, originated from ^{238}U. They comprise a number of elements, such as thorium, bismuth, polonium and even radium, but the ultimate stage of uranium decay is lead, which is stable and does not decay further. If we could wait long enough all the uranium would disappear and there would be nothing left but lead. However, by determining the present ratio of uranium and lead, which is a fairly simple process, we can find out how old the piece of mineral is without having to wait.

Once again we have here an opportunity of determining age by the radioactive decay of an isotope. If we compare this method with Libby's carbon clock we find a difference. Libby measured the residue of a radioisotope which is still being generated today, and he had at his disposal an extensive range of material which had already been dated by historians. For the determination of the earth's age, or rather the age of terrestrial minerals, we have only the residue of such radioactive isotopes as have been there since the earth was created, i.e., there are only continuously decreasing quantities. Hardly any control experiments are possible. Libby had substantial grounds for maintaining that the carbon-12/carbon-14 ratio had remained the same for tens of thousands of years. With geological material the problem is less simple. The substances had probably become hot and liquefied more than once. During such processes some components, such as lead, may have been extruded, other substances may have completely evaporated, or they may be found in adjoining rocks in a comparatively enriched mixture, or they may have been washed out of the rocks by water and deposited elsewhere. It is therefore necessary to be exceedingly careful in evaluating geological age data.

However, several methods are now available. If they all yield the same result for the same mineral we may be fairly sure that the answer is correct. Some figures, expressed in millions of years, for ores or minerals are shown below:

Trachyte from the Drachenfels on the Rhine	25
Pitchblende from Jachymov (Joachimsthal)	200
Some ore deposits from the Urals	240–270
Biotite from Dartmoor	270
Granite from Westmorland	381
Thorianite from Ceylon	500
African Morogoro ore	680
Bröggerite from Norway	900

From what moment can our planet be called "Earth"?

The ages of minerals quoted above seem astonishingly great, but they are fairly reliable.

By means of more perfected but basically similar techniques it is possible to date even older minerals. For instance, the age of lepidolite, found in various places in the United States and in Southern Rhodesia, has been determined as 2,550 and 2,640 million years.

The monazite sands in Southern Rhodesia are even older— 2,650 million years—and in the Transvaal the mineral uraninite was found to be 2,730 million years old. A rock fragment found on the Kola peninsula is 3,400 million years old. It should now be possible to discover the veritably "oldest" component of our earth.

Even so, there is no proof that these minerals originated during the formation of the earth. In fact, it is most unlikely that they are even approximately as old as the earth. Besides, one could argue about the point of time at which the earth could first be correctly given that name: when it was an almost shapeless cloud of, presumably, cosmic dust, or later, when the dust agglomerated and began to take shape. It would seem most reasonable to bestow a name on the accretion of matter when it had assumed a nearly spherical shape and showed signs of having a structure, even if it was possibly still semi-fluid. However, even the oldest known rock sample could not yet have existed in those far-off days; the firm crust of the earth probably took many more hundreds of million years to form.

If we are able to state with some certainty that the earth is older than 3,400 million years, and if we add another 1,000 million years for the preceding stage during which the minerals were solidifying into their present form, we arrive at a minimum age of at least 4,400 million years. That is probably an under-estimate, and we could, for reasons which will be explained later, add another 1,000 million years. But another question arises at this point: even if we ultimately discover the age of the earth, it does not mean that the universe is of the same age.

Paneth had a brilliant idea which enabled him to make a considerable contribution to the solution of this problem.

CHAPTER 3

A STONE DROPS FROM THE SKY

Wanted: meteorite chips. A star exploded fifty million
years ago.

AUGUST 11TH, 1956, was a fine summer's day, but otherwise it was like any other. At least so it remained at Breitscheid until the afternoon. A woman in that small village in Hessen in the Dillkreis district, 23 miles from the university town of Giessen, north of Frankfurt, had just finished her washing and was hanging it out to dry. The sky was clear, and somewhere a circling aircraft buzzed overhead. Suddenly something dropped from the sky a few paces in front of the woman and half-buried itself in the ground. Indignantly, she blamed the aircraft. How careless and dangerous to drop things like this. She approached the object, and discovered that it was a stone, a warm, large, black and rather heavy stone. Disgraceful! Dropping hot stones from an aircraft.

However, as such an occurrence was unusual at Breitscheid, she ended by taking the stone home. It became the talk of the village. Doubting peasants called and touched it, to convince themselves that it was a stone. They thought that it might be a piece of the aircraft. "Let's split it", was the natural reaction, and soon it was chipped into many fragments. The inside looked lighter in colour, the hard black crust was quite thin. All the woman's acquaintances and curious visitors took bits away with them as souvenirs, and the fragments found resting-places in drawers and boxes, alongside other knick-knacks and mementoes.

Soon it was forgotten. It was harvest-time, and the country-folk had plenty of other things to think about.

Then a chemist who worked in a factory near Breitscheid heard about the stone dropped from an aircraft and managed to obtain a chip. He split it, and analysed a sample. The stone turned out to be a meteorite. The chemist regarded this as quite an interesting occurrence, and wrote a short article about it in the *Dillpost*, the local newspaper, in the issue dated September 1st. The inhabitants of Breitscheid were relieved to

38

hear that nobody had been dropping stones on their village from an aircraft, and that the stone was a meteorite.

The local news editor of a Frankfurt newspaper read the article in the *Dillpost*, and decided that the incident would make a useful filler next time he was short of a couple of lines. On September 25th this occurred. The item was noticed by a woman chemist at the Max Planck Institute of Chemistry at Mainz, of which Paneth, the internationally known specialist on meteorite research, was director. Paneth found it difficult to believe the report. For years he had hoped to lay his hands on a recently fallen meteorite, because only such a messenger from outer space could help him to find the answer to a question which had puzzled him for a long time. He sent one of his assistants to Breitscheid next morning.

Wanted: meteorite chips

When Paneth left Vienna his outstanding qualifications took him as professor to Prague in 1918, then to Hamburg, then Berlin, and, in 1929, to Königsberg as a staff professor and director of the Chemical Institute of the university. In 1933, when future political events cast their shadows over Germany, Paneth was one of the first scientists to leave his country and go to Britain. For many years he remained in exile and, though friends helped him, found it hard to make ends meet. Finally, in the summer of 1953 he returned to Germany and became director of the Max Planck Institute in Mainz and head of the Chemistry Department.

While he was at Königsberg he began to take an interest in a field in which, according to current opinion, no more scientific fruits were to be gathered. It was generally agreed that everything about meteorites was known. Meteorites were large or small space vagabonds with surfaces that looked like the dark, sand-blasted bowl of a pipe. There were iron meteorites and stone meteorites, or a mixture of the two. Chemical analysis had shown that the composition of all meteorites was approximately the same. Meteorites fell from the sky and, if they were big enough, they could be found. Some museums pride themselves on having fine specimens, and museum directors shudder when they hear that some chemist is requesting a fragment for analysis.

However, contrary to the general opinion, Paneth found meteorites fascinating. During his stay in Britain he even published a book about them. He frequently said that what attracted him was the fact that meteorites were the only known fragments of heavenly bodies, the only extra-terrestrial matter we could actually handle.

Paneth's assistant returned from Breitscheid with two fragments of the stone, which was undoubtedly a meteorite. But where were the other fragments? From the moment when they realised that a meteorite was valuable, even if only scientifically valuable, the villagers of Breitscheid were on their toes, and the fragments that had wandered from hand to hand were suddenly called in by the "owners", regardless of whether they had originally been given away as presents. If the learned doctors in Mainz wanted them they must pay. Paneth paid. He paid by weight. The market price for meteorites at Breitscheid soared by leaps and bounds.

The meteorite was gradually reconstructed from the fragments, but one piece was still missing. Its owner, a girl from a neighbouring village, had taken it with her on holiday. When she was found she refused to part with it at any price.

Paneth, in a formal dark suit, called on the young lady. His old-world charm won her over, and a barter transaction was arranged, which was surely unique in scientific history. Paneth acquired the missing fragment in exchange for a necklace with a pendant containing a small chip. Paneth got the missing fragment, and the girl a piece of jewellery with a stone which was not of this earth.

A star exploded fifty million years ago

Why did Paneth want this meteorite as complete as possible? He wanted to find out whether this messenger from space was as old as terrestrial minerals, or perhaps even older. He already had an extensive list of age analyses of meteorites, but the values had been uncertain for a long time. Just as lead is the end product of uranium decay, helium is an inevitable by-product of this process, and the ratio between the two is known. The uranium content of a meteorite, together with its helium content, should therefore give a clue to its age. Strangely enough, the results achieved by this method remained unsatisfactory, since they varied too much. Eventually it became possible to show where the error lay. The assumption that the helium content was due entirely to uranium decay was wrong. In 1953 it was successfully demonstrated that up to 25 per cent of the discovered helium was not the helium-4 isotope, the product of uranium decay, but helium-3, which was generated under the influence of cosmic radiation during the passage of the meteorite through space. The proof was fairly simple: the outer layers of iron meteorites contained more helium-3 than the inner layers, which were less exposed to radiation in transit.

In addition, new and continuously perfected methods of age determination were developed, yielding meteorite ages up to 4,000 million years. These are relatively "reasonable" values, their order of magnitude corresponding to values established for the age of the earth. On the other hand, and this was decisive for Paneth, cosmic radiation forms, in addition to helium-3, many other isotopes, such as tritium, some of which have an extremely short life. The half-life of a certain sodium isotope is only about two and a half years. Paneth wanted to investigate these products, and for this purpose he needed complete meteorites, comprising both the outside shell and the inside core. Moreover, the meteorite had to be recent, otherwise the short-lived substances would have decayed to an extent which would have made their measurement no longer possible. Meteorite fragments out of museums were therefore of no use to him.

Paneth had the bold idea that the number and type of radioactive decay particles would tell the history of the meteorite. They would show how long the meteorite had been exposed to radiation in space and how strong that radiation had been. He hoped that one day it might be possible to chart the distribution of radiation in space. After meteorites had wandered about in space for millions of years they might yield some information, perhaps tell us where and how our planetary system originated. The first unexpected result of such research has shown that many of the hitherto analysed iron meteorites have been exposed to cosmic radiation for roughly a thousand million years, while stone meteorites have been exposed only for 10–300 million years.

Analysis of the Breitscheid meteorite yielded further interesting results. If all measurements derived from it are correct, and there are no reasons for doubting them, its material came from a celestial body which solidified about 3,000 million years ago, i.e., its rocks were younger than those of our earth. For some unknown reason, this cosmic rock mass exploded 50 million

41

years ago, and since then its fragments have been circling round the sun.

If we take into account the fact that meteorites can burst during their flight we can understand why the periods of exposure to cosmic rays vary so much. When a meteorite explodes, the resultant fragments have new, hitherto unexposed surfaces, and such fragments would naturally show a shorter exposure time to cosmic rays than a meteorite which had remained whole and whose surfaces had received continuous radiation. If all meteorites and their ages are listed together they are seen to divide into two groups:

(1) stone meteorites, exploded 10–300 million years ago, and

(2) iron–nickel meteorites which exploded at an earlier period, about 700–15,000 million years ago.

The age record is held at present by a meteorite which was tested by a process based on the presence of the radioactive isotope xenon-129. Like helium, xenon is a rare gas. The peculiarity of the isotope ^{129}Xe is that it originates from the decay of the iodine isotope of a mass of 129. This decay is so fast that it is not known on earth; it disappeared long ago. Therefore, if we can prove the presence of xenon-129 in a meteorite we are entitled to draw the conclusion that it originated at a time when there was still some iodine-129 about. Scientists claim to be able to tell from their measurements and calculations that the meteorite in question was formed 350 million years after the origin of iodine-129, i.e., after the origin of chemical elements in general.

The total age of this fragment of matter from space is calculated to be 4,950 million years, with a margin of error of 150 million years. This figure is the minimum possible age of our universe.

Today scientists, particularly those in the United States, are again intensively engaged on meteorite research, which was at one time regarded as having been completed. Two specialist international societies have been established, the members of which keep each other informed of meteorite falls in their countries. A few years ago a huge meteorite fell north-east of Vladivostok, displaying all the characteristics of an atomic explosion. It was a cataclysmic event. Was this the cause of the request that the United States stop the flights of their nuclear warhead aircraft? A fragment of this space "missile" is reported to have struck a ship. The Soviet Union issued a special postage stamp to commemorate the event. In accordance with the international agreement, Professor Paneth's institute received a fragment of this meteorite for research.

CHAPTER 4

COSMIC BOMBARDMENT

Giant craters exist not only on the moon. A meteorite indicator.
The riddle of the Nördlinger Ries valley. Cosmic chemistry.
Discoverer XVII under proton bombardment. The begin-
nings are not too remote.

OUR knowledge of the incidence of meteorites is very incomplete. The recorded falls of meteorites for the period 1388–1940
are as follows:

662 on the American continent;
335 in Europe;
226 in Asia;
91 in Australia;
71 in Africa.

The real figures are certainly higher. Sometimes hundreds
of "celestial stones" fall at once, and not always with as little
damage as at Breitscheid. On February 2nd, 1943, several
houses in the town of Carhuamayo in Peru were reported to
have been destroyed by meteorites. On October 18th, 1958, a
meteorite weighing nearly 18 lb, but of extraordinarily low
density, fell in central Sweden. The sacred stone of Hadjar al
Asuad, encased in silver and kept in the Ka'aba, the Moslems'
holy shrine at Mecca, is probably the most famous chunk of
meteorite iron. According to legend, the Archangel Gabriel
brought the stone to Ishmael when the Ka'aba was under construction, and it is said that the stone, which was originally
snow-white, turned black later because of the sins of the people.
On November 13th, 1835, "a large shining meteor" was
reported to have "set fire to a barn" near Belley in the department of the Aine, France.
Among the strangest meteorite falls were those at Bear Creek
in the United States and at Narraburra in Australia. The
American meteorite weighed 511 lb, and the Australian one
71 lb. Both were recorded, photographed and chemically
analysed, and it was discovered that they were so similar in
structure as well as in composition that they were assumed to

44

have been fragments of the same original stone. It is even possible that a third well-known meteorite was also a part of the same chunk.

In any case, meteorite falls are not as infrequent as is sometimes assumed. Just over a year after the fall of the Breitscheid meteorite, a scientist who worked at the Sonneberg observatory in Eastern Germany noticed a strange phenomenon in the sky as he was leaving the building at noon on December 6th, 1957. A silvery cloud formation appeared high in the cloudless sky, and two and a half minutes later he heard an explosive sound, followed by a thunder-like rumble. He wondered whether it was a jet aircraft or a meteor. Inquiries brought to light that the same, or similar, observations had been made at fifty-nine different localities. At first a red fireball was seen which grew brighter and brighter until it shone with bluish-white brilliance. A vapour trail started at an altitude of about 20 miles and ended at a height of about 10 miles. It was assumed that the meteor which left this trail during its passage fell near Oberhof in Thuringia. Some villages reported thunder so loud that the inhabitants believed that an earthquake was taking place, and some people even claimed to have noticed earth tremors. Naturally a search was made for the remnants of the meteorite, but a heavy fall of snow rendered the search difficult. It is doubtful whether fragments will now be found.

Giant craters exist not only on the moon

Since 1900 fragments of seven meteorites which had fallen in Germany have been found. The largest was the chunk of iron, weighing 138 lb, which fell near Treysa in Hessen in 1916.

Table of meteorite finds in Germany

Date	Place	Weight
June 12th, 1900	Forsbach near Cologne	8½ oz
April 3rd, 1916	Treysa near Marburg	138 lb
	(age about $1 \cdot 3 \cdot 10^9$ years)	
July 1st, 1920	Simmern, Hunsrück	1 lb 5½ oz; 15½ oz; 5 oz
December 30th, 1927	Oesede near Osnabrück	7 lb 6½ oz
September 10th, 1930	Beverbruch, Oldenburg	25 lb 11 oz; 10 lb 8 oz
August 11th, 1956	Breitscheid, Dillkreis	2 lb 3 oz
July 26th, 1958	Ramsdorf, Münster	10 lb 4½ oz

Searches have occasionally been made in other cases when the circumstances indicated meteorite falls, but no fragments were found. Unless many observers are in the open, as for instance during harvest-time, searches generally prove fruitless.

There are only a few recorded falls of very large meteorites. On June 30th, 1908, a large meteor allegedly fell in the Tunguska region of Siberia and caused damage spread over an area of 5,000 square miles. Apparently this space "missile" hit the earth at an angle. It is nonsense, however, to suppose that this feature and a few other circumstances indicate that this natural phenomenon was an emergency landing of an extra-terrestrial space ship.

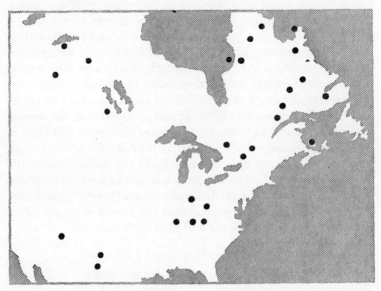

Map showing meteorite falls in North America

Today we can no longer doubt that the earth is sometimes struck by huge meteorites. The crater resulting from such an impact in Saskatchewan in Canada is more than 81 miles in diameter. The Vredefort Ring near Johannesburg in South Africa was probably caused by the impact of an enormous chunk of cosmic material. Strangely dislocated strata in this hollow were closely examined, and it was found that the meteorite impact had apparently caused deformation over an area nearly 137 miles across. It was assumed on the strength of the available evidence that a chunk approximately $1-1\frac{1}{4}$ miles in diameter came from a south-westerly direction and buried itself in the earth. Geological research disclosed that this truly cosmic event took place more than 250,000 years ago and

46

released vast amounts of energy. The earthquake which must have followed this impact was indubitably many times greater than any recorded in historical times. Another remarkable feature noted by the experts is the peculiar orientation of the Belcher Islands in Hudson Bay, which are located in a circle 250 miles in diameter. This suggests the possibility that they are the highest peaks of a ring of mountains thrown up by a giant meteorite.

Perhaps this problem will be solved in a few years, because a test for determining meteorite impacts has recently been devised. Its history starts with a synthetic mineral called coesite.

A meteorite indicator

A few years ago L. Coes, Jr., an American scientist, investigated what happened to minerals when subjected to very high pressures and temperatures. In the course of this work he succeeded, in 1953, in producing a new mineral from quartz, and this mineral was subsequently called coesite after him. Why had this mineral not been found in nature? It was assumed that this variety of quartz could be found only in the depths of the earth, because high pressures were required for its generation. The search for coesite in South African diamond mines and other places was unsuccessful, and it was concluded that it did not exist in a natural state.

In 1960 this assumption was disproved. Dr. E. M. Shoemaker, of Washington, was investigating the well-known meteorite crater in Arizona, a hollow 580 feet deep and $\frac{3}{4}$ mile wide. The legends of the Hopi Indians speak of the fiery descent from heaven of one of their gods to that spot. The first white settlers who came into the area found numerous metal fragments in the crater, and concluded that a "star" had fallen there.

Today it is estimated that the meteorite which caused the Barringer Crater in Arizona fell to earth 25,000 years ago. This makes the Indian legend rather incredible.

Geologists regard the Arizona crater as the "classic" meteorite crater. Most of its walls consist of sandstone, and its bottom is strewn with rocks. The enormous heat generated by the impact of the meteorite melted some of the sandstone into vitreous fragments. Rock débris thrown upwards by the force of the impact are scattered about the crater walls. In this crater Shoemaker found a mineral which proved to be identical with the synthetic coesite. In many ways the meteorite impact must have been more powerful than a nuclear bomb. So far no coesite has been found after any nuclear-bomb tests.

Coesite must now be classed not only as a naturally occurring mineral but also as an indicator of meteorite impacts. Wherever coesite occurs on the earth's surface it probably owes its origin to a meteorite fall in that locality.

The riddle of the Nördlinger Ries valley

Dr. Shoemaker reported on his Arizona investigations at the International Geological Congress in Stockholm in 1960. He wanted to take the opportunity of this trip to Europe to solve a very old geological problem, and before the congress therefore went to Nördlingen. The Suabian and the Franconian Alps are separated here by a valley called Nördlinger Ries, which

The Ries Valley between the Suabian and Franconian Alps

has attracted geologists from all over the world again and again, for there seems to be no reasonable explanation for its existence in the midst of a succession of mountain ridges. What was its origin? For a long time a big volcanic eruption was put forward as a possible explanation. However, in the 'thirties the idea arose that the valley might be the crater of a huge meteorite. The valley is about 15 miles in diameter, and under its surface layer of loess clay there is a mixture of granite rocks of the Jurassic and Triassic periods. Unlike the Arizona crater,

48

A piece of pre-Ice Age timber from Ohio, older than 20,000 years. Next to it, human hair from Egypt, 5,020 ($\pm$ 290) years old

A rope from Peru, 2,632 ($\pm$ 200) years old

Prof. F. A. Paneth, German chemist and meteorite investigator, of the Max Planck Institute of Chemistry, Mainz (died 1958)

Photo:

A fragment of the Breitscheid meteorite, weighing about 5 oz. The thin, black outer layer is clearly visible on top

the crater's edge is very indistinct. The vitreous fragments and granite rock débris of the Ries are, however, similar to Shoemaker's finds in the Arizona crater. Moreover, the analysis of these finds also disclosed coesite. The latter mineral is so common here that, in Dr. Shoemaker's estimate, the walls of St. George's Church at Nördlingen, built in the fifteenth century from local stone, contain more than a ton of coesite.

Whether the smaller valley known as the Steinheimer Becken, near Heidenheim, 21 miles south of the Ries valley, has any connection with the meteorite fall has yet to be investigated. It is possible that both valleys were caused by the same meteorite.

The Arizona crater is undoubtedly fairly new, geologically speaking. The Nördlinger Ries is estimated to be much older, about 15–20 million years.

The interest of geologists was naturally concentrated on the impressive Arizona crater and the strange Ries valley, particularly as these localities indicated the fall of very large meteorites. Could the coesite test for meteorites be applied, however, also to smaller impacts?

Scientists found a small valley, hardly more than a round trough, near Al Hadida in Saudi Arabia (21° 30′ N., 50° 28′ E.). Its diameter is about 330 feet and its depth about 42 feet. Sand had covered up all details long ago. Nevertheless, fragments of a blackish, vitreous substance were found among sandstone débris. The analysis of some samples indicated 1 per cent coesite. There is no doubt that here too the earth was hit by a meteorite.

This showed that smaller meteorite falls could also be substantiated. In a few years it may be possible to include meteorite impact charts in our atlases.

Cosmic chemistry

The question arises: since when have meteorites been striking the earth? If there were meteorite falls during the early ages of the earth's history these must now be hidden in ancient geological rock layers. Since the beginning of human history stone has been quarried for buildings, roads and other purposes, but there was until recently no record of a meteorite having ever been found in such strata. A most extraordinary chance, however, gave a hint of their existence. Recently an oil well was being drilled in Texas, and at a depth of 1,640 feet the drill

D 49

encountered resistance and then got stuck. When finally the obstacle was overcome and the core fragments were brought up for examination they turned out to be iron. Now, the natural presence of iron in the kind of strata being drilled was out of the question. Chemical analysis confirmed the only possible solution of the puzzle; the drill had struck an embedded iron meteorite, composed of 82 per cent iron, 5–10 per cent nickel, and some traces of phosphorus, carbon and silicon. The geological environment of this find proved incontrovertibly that meteorites had reached the earth as far back as the Tertiary period, i.e., the period when the Alps were formed, the Eifel, Vogelsberg and Rhön areas in Germany were still volcanic, and hot springs shot up, such as we still know of at Baden-Baden in the Rhine valley, which at that time was still in process of formation.

A new, but quite natural branch of chemistry, "cosmic chemistry", is now beginning to develop. We still have no suitable name for the science of the soil and minerals of extraterrestrial bodies, but in the foreseeable future we are likely to have a lunar "geology". We must, however, wait for this until the first moon rockets bring back samples from the lunar surface. Even before that event, rockets will have enabled us to learn more about the distribution of meteors in space. Thus, it is already possible to record the impact of micrometeors on space probes, and space vehicles and probes are now fitted with meteor "traps". These devices allow us to determine several properties of meteors, such as their frequency, the direction and speed of their flight and, within certain margins of error, even their mass.

Discoverer XVII under proton bombardment

In future meteorite scientists and space pilots will work together in other respects, too. At 12.42 p.m. on November 12th, 1960, the satellite Discoverer XVII was launched from the Vandenberg base in California. This happened while an enormous gas eruption was taking place on the sun and was subjecting the earth to an extensive bombardment of solar protons. The satellite circled the earth for two days at an altitude of between 125 and 565 miles. When it came down over the Pacific it was found to be radioactive. Immediate investigation of the nuclear-chemical changes that had occurred was carried out and produced a number of interesting results. For instance, it was found that each square inch of the satellite's surface had been hit by over 600 million protons. If we consider that the composition of iron–nickel meteorites is in many ways similar to that of stainless steel, the structural material of the satellite, the connection is clear. Satellites can give us information about what can occur in space during brief periods of radiation, while meteorites can show us only what occurs during prolonged flights in outer space. The utilisation, for research purposes, of meteorites, the "space ships of the poor" as they have been called, is, of course, more difficult, but the results are hardly less fascinating.

This, however, raises an important objection to all attempts at dating. The same objection had already been raised against Libby's carbon-14 dating method. All such methods assume that radiation eruptions, such as that recorded by Discoverer XVII, have had no important effect, because, if the intensity of cosmic radiation has varied, or even only fluctuated about the normal level, errors in dating are inevitable. Can we be sure that there were no fluctuations? At first Libby could not counter this objection. However, there was no need for him to do so, because he had the opportunity of demonstrating that, in the case of long time periods, his method agreed accurately with accepted data of the historians.

The position is more difficult, however, in regard to terrestrial minerals. One could, of course, see whether the dating agreed with that determined by the geologists from the successions of strata. However, as regards the actual age of an individual layer, the geologists prefer to ask the physicists rather than be guided purely by mineralogical finds. As far as meteorites are concerned, it was necessary for a long time to assume that cosmic radiation was constant in time. Today we know that this is actually the case. Meteorites were subjected experimentally to a fairly good imitation of cosmic proton radiation. Afterwards the ratio of the resultant quantity of argon-39 and chlorine-36 was determined, and scientists drew the conclusion that for at least several million years the intensity of cosmic radiation had not deviated on the average by more than 10 per cent from that observed today.

The beginnings are not too remote

We now have a well-founded and scientifically accurate time scale, reaching back over decades, centuries, millennia and millions of years, to the remotest times of the origin of the earth and the universe, and we have found that there are now no unbridgeable gaps in the chronicle of the earth. Dating techniques will undoubtedly be further developed and improved. In addition to the older chemical, physical and biological methods, increasing use is made of new techniques, such as the carbon-14 and tritium methods, using isotopes formed by cosmic radiation. Suitable isotopes for this purpose suggest themselves:

> Beryllium-10, half-life 2,700,000 years;
> Silicon-32,   ,,   710   ,,

Indeed, silicon-32 promises important results. It is taken up by sponges, diatoms and radiolaria, i.e., marine animals, and it is believed that information about sea deposits and the movement of marine sediments can ultimately be obtained, and other oceanological problems solved. However, here too the effect of nuclear tests is hazardous. If we estimate the existing terrestrial amount of silicon-32 derived from cosmic radiation we arrive at a total of not quite 4 lb. As this amount is relatively small, any silicon-32 generated by an atomic explosion can falsify the measurements very considerably.

However, apart from the length of the time period under consideration, and the astonishing absence of gaps in our knowledge as we survey it, we have to face the fact that the past has a limit. The estimate may vary by a few million years (this will be discussed more fully in subsequent chapters), but the past is not infinite. The earth and the sun have not existed eternally.

II

Let there be light: and there was light
Genesis I. 3

The Book of Genesis tells us in detail about the
creation of the earth, but very little about the origin of
the star-studded sky. It almost seems that the sky's
only purpose is to give light to the earth.

Is the earth really the most important part of
creation? Scientists deny it. Even our vast solar system is only a dot in the universe.

There are many mysteries on earth which we are
still incapable of solving. The concept that our universe may possibly have a counterpart, an anti-
universe, adds to the confusion.

CHAPTER 5

THE GREAT CELESTIAL
MERRY-GO-ROUND

Kepler's law of planetary motion. How long is a light year?
Behind a pillar of the great world theatre.

JOHANNES KEPLER's mother has been described as quarrelsome, gossip-loving and rather simple-minded. His father, a descendant of an impoverished Suabian noble family named von Kappel, was not much better. He spent most of his life roaming about as a mercenary. In 1574 he was in the Netherlands, in 1577 in Belgian service, finally he was reported to have taken part in a naval war on the side of the Neapolitans. After this all trace of him is lost. If it were necessary to quote an example of a genius emerging from a poor background, this case would serve.

Leonberg, Magstadt and the town of Weil, all of them in Württemberg, quarrelled for a long time about the honour of being Kepler's birthplace. He himself stated that he was born on December 27th, 1571, in the ancient town of Weil, the eldest of seven children. He was a sickly child, and his father despised him from the beginning, and forced him to work as a servant in an inn which he was temporarily managing. It was Johannes Kepler's grandfather who encouraged him and arranged for him to be educated. Kepler discovered his love of astronomy while a theological student at Tübingen. Although he obtained his master's degree with distinction, his scientific ideas and his adherence to the new Copernican system placed him in sharp opposition to the Church. He was therefore sent to Styria, which was regarded as liberal and tolerant, and he became a teacher of mathematics at Graz. Though he considered astrology to be nonsense, he was obliged to provide astrological predictions every year for the local calendar. He "predicted" peasant revolts, Turkish invasions and cold winters. It is doubtful whether he would have been pleased if his predictions had come true, but they spread his reputation, and so he acquired private clients who ordered horoscopes from him. Thus, his financial position improved and he was able to devote himself seriously to astronomy. His own comment was: "Mother Astronomy would certainly have to go hungry if her daughter Astrology were not the breadwinner."

Dark times came, however. Religious freedom was abolished in Styria. Domestic squalor and, finally, the impounding of his property, forced Kepler to escape while there was still time. Tycho Brahe, the famous court astronomer of the Emperor Rudolph II, had heard of Kepler and invited him to Prague to be his assistant. After Brahe's death in 1601 Kepler took his place, but the exalted rank of court astronomer provided no living, as the Emperor's exchequer was exhausted, and again Kepler was in financial straits. His wife and child died. The Emperor Matthias, Rudolph's successor, had no use for an astronomer. Kepler went to Linz as a teacher of mathematics, but under the pressure of the Counter-Reformation had to give up this humble job. His writings were publicly burned. His mother was accused of witchcraft and put in chains. She died in 1619, shortly after her release, for which her son fought for years. Wallenstein, the Commander of the Emperor's forces, arranged for Kepler to stay in Sagan in Silesia for two years. In 1630, at the age of sixty, Kepler rode on horseback to the Reichstag in Regensburg with the intention of claiming 12,000 guilders as arrears in salary, and of finding a new homeland for his family. He died in Regensburg on November 15th, without achieving either aim, and as a stranger to the town he was buried outside the walls.

The Inquisition directed its onslaught against Kepler and his contemporary Galileo, since Copernicus, the real originator of the "new teaching", was beyond their reach. Nicholas Copernicus, Canon in Frauenburg, West Prussia, a man of breeding and education with wide spiritual and worldly interests, knew what the attitude of the Church would be to such a revolutionary view of the universe, and had therefore been cautious. He was an honourable man, but liked his peace and sought neither fame nor enmity. For forty years he left unpublished the vast intellectual edifice later known as the Copernican System. In response to his friends' pressure he finally sent his work *On the Rotation of Celestial Bodies* to the printers, and on the day of his death received the first copy of his great book. He seemed to foresee that the publication of his heliocentric picture of the universe would call forth, not only amazement but fear, for in the introduction he wrote:

"All this, difficult and almost incomprehensible as it may appear to some, and contrary to the views of the majority, all this we shall explain with God's help in the course of this work and make clearer than the sun, at least for those who are not devoid of all mathematical knowledge."

The majority of his contemporaries did not understand his writings, and even the nimble-witted inquisitors, who smelled heresy and impermissible novelty everywhere, could not follow the thought of this cleric who was as diplomatic as he was learned. In order to placate the Protestants, who also found the theory of the moving earth objectionable, Andreas Osiander, a Lutheran preacher at the famous St. Lawrence church in Nuremberg, claimed, in a kind of editor's preface, that Copernicus's ideas were purely hypothetical. Seventy years after the epoch-making work appeared in print the world and the Church realised what had happened. He had displaced the earth from the centre of the universe and "degraded" it to a subordinate position in the solar system. This removal of the earth from its central position could be interpreted only as the removal of man from the proximity of God. The very thought was heresy. In 1616 the book was put on the Index.

In defence of divine omnipotence and papal authority the Church insisted on the correctness of the geocentric picture of the universe put forward by Claudius Ptolemy of Alexandria (87–165) and propounded, partly intuitively and partly for theoretical reasons, by the pre-Christian Greek philosophers. The ancients' view of the universe was based on their deep reverence for geometry, particularly for the circle. Aristotle (384–322 B.C.) taught:

"The shape of the dome of heaven is of necessity globular, for the globe is the most suitable shape. Planets move in circles round the earth, for the circle is the paramount shape of all shapes. The globe and the circle are paramount. . . ."

For about a millennium and a half hardly any new theories were proposed. The earth stood still, and everything moved around it. Man ruled the earth and therefore he too was in the centre of the universe, and God was next to him.

Copernicus's doctrine was banned, but no power on earth could prevent its eventual victory. Exactly one hundred years after its publication, Galileo Galilei, a merchant's son from

Pisa, a mathematician and physicist as well as an astronomer, managed adroitly to put over the new view of the universe by making use of his excellent connections. In the preface to his book about the two "systems" of the universe he expressed approval of the Church's condemnation of Copernicus, but throughout the book he maintained the opposite. When, however, in 1632 he succeeded in publishing his book with the permission of the Inquisitor of Florence, he strained his good fortune to breaking-point. His friend, Cardinal Maffeo Barberini, who had meanwhile become Pope Urban VIII, summoned him before the Inquisition. It was probably thanks to him that Galileo got off so lightly. On June 20th, 1633, he had to make a solemn recantation. The story of his jumping to his feet immediately afterwards, stamping his foot and exclaiming, *Eppur si muove* ("And yet it moves!") is apocryphal. However, there is no doubt that inwardly he was convinced of it.

Kepler's law of planetary motion

Kepler made hardly any observations of the sky himself. Never in his life could he afford materials for the construction of a good telescope. Besides, his eyesight was too bad for this sort of work, as it had been affected by smallpox in his youth.

He relied on Tycho Brahe's observations, which, indeed, were excellent. Kepler's first book, written at Graz, dealt with the mysticism of geometrical shapes and was highly speculative, but by 1609, when his *Astronomica nova* appeared, he had grown out of the fanciful kind of writing. From Brahe's observations he was able to calculate that the earth moved, not in a circle, but in an ellipse, and that its speed varied in the course of the year. His favourite work *Harmonici mundi* appeared in 1619 and discussed the relation between the rotation periods of the planets and their distance from the sun. He propounded the three famous Keplerian laws:

1. Each planet moves in an ellipse with the sun at one focus.
2. For each planet the line from the sun to the planet sweeps out equal areas in equal times.
3. The squares of the periodic times of the planets are proportional to the cubes of their mean distances from the sun.

Kepler went on publishing. He was an excellent observer, and wrote of what he saw. He wrote a book on the laws of optics, discourses on the hexagonal shape of snow-flakes, on the telescope, on mathematical problems, lightning, thunder and comets.

In 1606 he started a disputation about the date of Christ's birth. He claimed that it differed by six years from the generally accepted date, because he believed that a very rare conjunction of Jupiter and Saturn in the Pisces sign of the Zodiac had been the Star of Bethlehem. This kind of conjunction takes place every 258 years (it will occur again in 2198) and, according to Kepler's calculations, it took place in 7 B.C. Today, with a margin of error of one or two days, we can date the appearance of the conjunction over the Bethlehem stable as having occurred on December 4th, 7 B.C. If we wished to be precisely accurate we should celebrate Christmas on December 4th, a date which is also supported by the "Augustinian Testament", an inscription in the Augustus and Roma temple in Ankara, and by the cuneiform scripts of the astrology school at Sippar in Babylonia.

How interesting even the lesser-known writings of Kepler are today has been shown by the recent reprinting in Berlin of his brief paper on the hexagonal shape of snow. Incidentally, it was Kepler who coined the word "satellite", which he used for the moons of Jupiter.

Was there good cause for accusing Kepler of heresy? From the point of view of his contemporaries there certainly was. From Kepler's own point of view, such accusations were quite absurd. It was true that, in his opinion, the Bible was inaccurate, but, so far as he was conerned, that was no reason for doubting the basic principles of the Christian faith. On the contrary, he had demonstrated the power and order and geometry of creation more clearly than anyone before him.

Kepler was greatly fascinated by the movements of planets round the sun. His joy in their orderly progression undoubtedly gave him strength to endure his fate. They displayed the rigid forms of a divine geometry, and he saw creation in its full and everlasting beauty.

It is a matter for speculation whether he would have had the same strength to endure his fate if he could have foreseen the true size of the celestial sphere and the multiplicity of different problems which his theories would create for scientists.

59

If we wish to determine the distance between ourselves and a certain object, we measure as accurately as possible the distance between two accessible points. This distance is termed the "base". Then, from each of the accessible points, we measure the angle between the other accessible point and the distant object. Everyone knows that from these data the distance to the object can then be determined, for example, by drawing them as a triangle. However, this method is useless if the base at our disposal is too small in comparison with the distance which we wish to measure.

Friedrich Wilhelm Bessel, a Königsberg astronomer, was the first to use, in 1838, the longest possible base for determining the distance of stars. He used the diameter of the earth's orbit round the sun. A surveyor has to walk from one measurement point to the next along his base line, but Bessel used the earth itself as a "means of transport" along his base line. He measured the angle of a certain star, and in the next six months was carried by the earth to another point in the universe from which he again measured the angle of the same star.

The star he selected for this purpose is in the Cygnus constellation and is known to astronomers as 61 Cygni. He calculated its distance from the earth as 64,680,000 million miles. A distance of such magnitude is inconceivable to the ordinary mind. We can grasp it no better if we are told that it is 690,000 times that between the earth and the sun. G. Gamow, the American physicist, once quoted a more easily grasped example: If the sun were as large as a pumpkin, the earth in proportion would be as large as a pea circling the pumpkin at a distance of 233 feet. The moon would be barely visible, being the size of a poppy seed. There would then be a distance of 20,000 miles between our pea and 61 Cygni. The speed of light (~186,000 miles per second) is considered as the absolute limit of speed. This figure, again, is difficult to imagine. It may be clearer if we visualise the following: a flash of light can circle the earth seven and a half times in a second. It takes a little more than a second to reach the moon, and it takes eight minutes to reach the sun, but it takes about eleven years to reach 61 Cygni. If this star perished in a catastrophe today it would be eleven years before the astronomers noticed that its light was missing from the sky. To make the astronomical distances more manageable, we say that the star is eleven light years away; one light year is nearly 6 million million miles.

Later, other ways of measuring astronomical distances were found. Bessel's method was a brilliant flash of genius in his time. He wrote about it to John Herschel, the British astronomer who worked on the cataloguing of stars. John Herschel was the famous son of an even more famous father, William Herschel, a military musician from Hanover who deserted during the Seven Years' War, and at first made an inadequate living as a music teacher in England. He is mentioned here not merely because as an amateur astronomer he discovered the planet Uranus on March 13th, 1781. This achievement gained him the interest of the King, as well as a rich wife. He did more than that; his home-made reflecting telescope enabled him to make an even more important discovery which he reported to the Royal Society in 1784: "The so-called Milky Way is a very extensive layer of stars, of which our sun and our solar system are but a part."

Behind a pillar of the great world theatre

The importance of the earth, and of man living on it, had shrunk again. Man was no longer the inhabitant of a com-

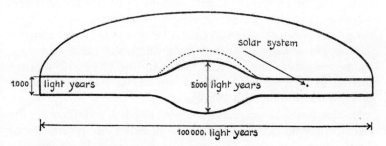

Position of our solar system in a schematic diagram of the Milky Way

paratively large planet of a central sun. The sun was merely an unimportant star in the Milky Way—at a generous estimate, only one among about 40 million others. Even the solar system was pushed out of its comparatively central position. It is part of a formation which, if we could see it from outside, is a roughly lentil-shaped galaxy, 100,000 light years in diameter, 1,000–5,000 light years thick.

According to man's earlier stage of knowledge, he was a traveller in a kind of double merry-go-round, the earth turning on its north–south axis and simultaneously round the sun. Then a third movement was added. Our solar system, together with countless thousands of other solar systems, revolves round some centre in the Milky Way. We do not know exactly where this centre is, but it is somewhere in the Sagittarius region. We cannot see it; we have a bad seat in the theatre of the universe—behind a pillar, so to speak, for dark clouds of cosmic matter float between us and the centre, and cut off the light. The rotation velocities of our super merry-go-round are quite considerable. On our earth we are whirled around at a speed of about 1,037 miles an hour on the equator. At the same time we circle round the sun at $18\frac{1}{2}$ miles a second. The velocity of the rotation of our galaxy, however, is 140 miles a second. Thus, we need 200 million years to complete the orbit.

If the universe were empty but for our galaxy we could perhaps still retain a glimmer of pride and self-esteem. Unfortunately this is not the case. For scores of years astronomers have observed tiny nebulous patches in the sky. Their distance could not be determined, and so they were considered "tiny", but this idea was radically changed when new instruments and methods were developed. There is no need to go into details here, let it suffice to note that these tiny spots are other Milky Ways, i.e., other spiral galactic nebulae, just like ours. Their shapes differ, and so does their size; some are denser than others, some have a spiral, fringed edge. An estimate has been made of the number of these galaxies by counting those observable in a certain section of the sky and deducing the total with a fairly narrow margin of error. There are about a million million galaxies within our optical horizon.

In the last few years radioastronomy has obtained results which allow us more accurately to describe our position, i.e., the position of our solar system, in our galaxy. If we imagine that we are looking from "above" at the wide surface of our spiral galactic nebula, we would see in the centre a kind of luminous patch, such as we can observe in the centre of a whirling Catherine Wheel firework. However, our "Catherine Wheel" is very large; a ray of light which, as we said above, travels at the rate of 186,000 miles a second would take 10,000 years to traverse the central section alone. The central area is surrounded by four to five almost circular spiral arms. These are generally frayed-looking trails of stars and stellar matter, with occasional thicker clusters. The spacing between the spiral arms of the galaxy is irregular, and the distances between them increase towards the outer periphery. The outer fringes look splayed out and ragged. Our solar system rotates within one of the thick clusters of one of the spirals, 27,000 light years from the centre of the galactic system. There are spiral nebulae with larger central areas than our galaxy, and with better defined and more numerous spirals. On the other hand, other nebulae have smaller centres and only two frayed spiral arms. Our galaxy is midway between these two extremes, and is of a fairly widespread type. Astronomers class it among spiral nebulae designated as "Sb".

Our past experience suggests the question whether all these giant worlds rotate round a common centre, or whether some of them belong to a rotating system which, in turn, rotates round another centre. We wish to know if there is any end to this super merry-go-round, and what the size of the universe is.

The answers to all these questions belong to the realm of speculation. Another figure will illustrate the immensity of the problem. The nearest galactic system to our own is 1,500,000 light years away. What we see today as a very distant nebula is a thing of the past; we see it as it was 1,500,000 years ago. We could find out what it is like today only by waiting for another 1,500,000 years. There is no point in labouring the futility of this argument.

CHAPTER 6

THE EXPANDING UNIVERSE

*The universe is exploding in all directions. A film run off in
reverse. We are eye-witnesses of creation.*

No sooner had astronomy reduced the earth to insignificance
among the countless spiral nebulae in the vast distances of cosmic space than scientists were confronted with a discovery
which again put the earth in the centre of cosmic events. This
was one of the most fundamental discoveries in the history of
astronomy, and is inseparably connected with the name of
the American astronomer Edward P. Hubble.

Hubble, whose ancestors had emigrated to the New World
from Cromwell's England, was born in 1889 at Marshfield,
Missouri. His father was a lawyer. When the family moved to
a suburb of Chicago Hubble started attending Chicago University. His interest in astronomy and mathematics was matched
by his interest in sport. It was typical of America, the country
of unlimited opportunities, that a promoter who saw Hubble
at an amateur boxing contest suggested training him with a
view to his fighting Jack Johnson, then heavyweight champion
of the world. However, Hubble decided against the professional
boxing ring, but did not immediately devote himself to astronomy. He broke off his natural science studies, left his famous
teachers Millikan and Hale, and went to Britain to study law.
On his return to the United States he started practising as an
attorney at Louisville, Kentucky. But after a year he had had
enough of this kind of law. The laws governing the celestial
spheres attracted him more. He obtained a post at Yerkes
Observatory and, in 1916, he published his work on the photographic investigation of faint nebulae, i.e., very distant galaxies.
A short time after joining the observatory he obtained the
degree of doctor of philosophy. His future as an astronomer
seemed to be settled when suddenly he became a soldier, for the
United States had entered the war. However, with an eye to
the future, he sent a telegram to his old teacher Hale, asking
whether he could work at the Mount Wilson Observatory after
the conclusion of hostilities.

The Mount Wilson Observatory in California had at that time the world's largest telescope, a gift of the Carnegie Trust, which spent the enormous sum of $10 million on it. It was this telescope which Hubble pointed in the direction of the thousands of known nebulae. The great nebula in the Andromeda constellation aroused his particular interest. This nebula is named Messier 31, after a famous astronomer. Hubble wished to know the distance to this stellar system, and he evolved a new method for determining it. The distance of some kinds of stars can be determined from variation in their brightness. Hubble's calculations showed the distance of Messier 31 to be about 900,000 light years. Further observation showed that the Great Nebula in Andromeda was a galaxy of stars similar in size and distribution to our own Milky Way.

The universe is exploding in all directions

One of the results of determining the distances of remote galaxies led to sensational conclusions: all the galaxies so far investigated are moving away from our earth, rushing into space in all directions.

It had been observed long ago that, for instance, the whistle of a rapidly approaching locomotive is raised in pitch. When the locomotive has passed us the pitch falls. The engine driver hears the whistle at a steady, fixed pitch in the medium range. A similar observation can be made in regard to the engine noise of a car driven at speed. The cause of these phenomena had been recognised and described in 1841 by Christian Doppler, a physicist working in Prague, and it is now known as the Doppler effect. The explanation is simple. As the vehicle approaches us the sound waves are crowded together, i.e., they become shorter, and as the vehicle travels away from us they spread out and become longer. We hear short sound waves as high-pitched sounds and long sound waves as low-pitched sounds.

Light too consists of waves. If, for instance, a luminous rocket were fired at tremendous speed from the moon in the direction of the earth, we should see its light as a whitish-violet. If a similar rocket were fired in the other direction it would appear more reddish, for violet corresponds to short, and red to long, light waves.

Hubble's observations demonstrated that the light of the observed stars is invariably moving towards red. Moreover, and this is even more decisive, the greater the distance of a star, the more pronounced is the shift towards red. Only one conclusion is possible: the farther the stars, the greater the velocity at which they are receding from us.

An increasing number of stars is being investigated, and Hubble and his colleagues are continuously faced with the question of whether a new calculation or observation will confirm the earlier conclusions or otherwise. A single exception would destroy this new picture of an expanding universe. However, no exception has yet been found. As the distance from the earth increases, the velocities with which everything moves away from us becomes staggeringly great.

The highest velocity measured so far belongs to a cosmic body which can be photographed only with difficulty as a tiny smudge by the large telescope of the Mount Palomar Observatory. From its red shift a velocity of 90,000 miles a second was calculated, i.e., 46 per cent of the speed of light. The estimated distance of this object is even more fantastic; astronomers believe it to amount to 6 million light years.

Is our galaxy, then, really the centre of the universe? Are man and earth really in a privileged position? Was the earth and its environment the first to be created?

The reply of the scientists is an unqualified no. The whole universe is expanding. We receive the impression that everything is moving away from us into infinite space, as if we were the centre. However, if there were an astronomer on an "earth" of another galaxy his observation would be exactly the same. He, too, would imagine that his "earth" was the centre and that everything was moving away from him.

Proper understanding of this paradox can be achieved only by introducing abstruse mathematical concepts. However, in order to obtain at least some picture of the process, we should consider the case of a partly inflated toy balloon. A group of, say, ten points are marked on it with ink. If we choose one of these points as representing our galaxy and then further inflate the balloon all the other dots will be seen to move away from "our galaxy" dot.

No matter which dot on the balloon surface we choose as "our galaxy", the others will move away from it when the "universe" expands. This may be easier to grasp than a full mathematical explanation.

66

The fascination that the idea of the expanding universe has for astronomers is easy to understand. Having recognised the process taking place, they are able to predict what the universe will look like in, say, a million years. What the world was like millions of years ago is a far more interesting question. We have, of course, to assume that the laws which have so far been deduced from the measurements are "eternally" valid and are not subject to changes of which we have no knowledge, because we have studied the subject for a few scores of years only.

On this basis we are bound to conclude that millions of years ago the distances between the individual galaxies were smaller. Their recession velocities must necessarily have been smaller, too. If we go even farther back into the past there must have been a time when the galaxies were all quite close together. The story is like a film which is being projected in reverse. Physicists have calculated the processes and their duration and have come to a staggering conclusion: about 4,000 million years ago the universe must have been a single blob of matter. This distant date seems plausible in view of the conclusions reached about the age of our own earth and the age of meteorites, as well as the estimated age of other stars.

It is true that no experiment can be mounted which would incontrovertibly prove these conclusions, but all pieces of the jigsaw fit neatly together, and the resulting picture is so complete that we are bound to accept it.

Moreover, we have one item of confirmation. According to ancient Chinese writings, in the year 1054 of our calendar a new brilliant star appeared suddenly in the sky. In 1572 Tycho Brahe observed a similar phenomenon, and Kepler saw a new star in 1604. These new stars flared up, became duller in the course of a few months, and then gradually decreased in luminosity. Today we have records of a large number of such events. In July, 1959, the Mount Palomar Observatory reported that one of the million suns in the NGC 7331 spiral nebula suddenly increased in brightness a hundred thousand times or so. Had the star exploded? For a long time people believed that this was the case. However, an explosion is not the only possible explanation, at least not in every case. On the contrary, new stars are formed by the condensation of cosmic matter. Many stars are much younger than the earth. Many familiar constellations may not be older than the first appearance of our ancestors on earth.

We are eye-witnesses of creation

It is very difficult to estimate how many new stars are formed and how large they are. The physicist Pascual Jordan attempted an estimate. Once the order of magnitude of the rate of creation of new matter is ascertained, the "film of creation" can be run off in reverse. Reaching millions and billions of years back into the past, Jordan's calculations showed that the mass of stellar material decreased as he went back in time. In reply to a question about the size of the universe when it was only ten seconds old, Pascual Jordan gave an exact answer: about as large as the sun. His calculations also showed that the amount of matter in the world at that moment was smaller than the mass of the moon.

Jordan's next question may seem presumptuous, but he asked it all the same: What was the world like a fraction of a second after it was created? According to his findings, it consisted of two elementary atomic particles. He assumed that they were both neutrons.

Astronomers and physicists everywhere discuss the measurements and interpretations of Hubble and his group. Scientists are sceptical. They are always particularly suspicious of any theory into which everything seems to fit as smoothly as it does into this picture of the world. Certainly Hubble's measurements have been repeated with the same results. It seems reasonable to accept a theory which brings things together in an explicable relationship, and yet—is there no possibility of another, even better, interpretation?

Criticisms of Hubble's interpretation of his findings therefore continue to be made. The assumptions behind them are by no means baseless, but experimental verification of them is slender. Their profoundest justification is the fact that man, living on earth, has necessarily acquired his entire knowledge of physics on earth. Everything investigated and measured so far has been subject to terrestrial atmospheric pressure and gravity, and to average temperature limits. By means of intricate and imaginative technical devices physicists have contrived to extend the field of measurement by a few thousand degrees, and increase the atmospheric pressure a few thousand times. Nevertheless, experiments are still limited to a relatively narrow range, and we must not forget that, in principle, a different kind of physics, chemistry and mechanics is a possibility under different, i.e., extra-terrestrial, conditions. At present we still have no confirmation of this, but basically the idea cannot be rejected. If, however, it is not "forbidden" to think in this way some ideas about "space", outer space, will not be out of place. We have measured a few things in space, but we have made no active, i.e., purposeful experiments there, experiments which aim at answers to definite questions. Even in this rocket age of ours, space is still the great unknown. What we know for certain is that space is not empty, but full of matter in the form of stars, and that it is traversed by forces of gravitational and electromagnetic nature. What happens to the light of the stars during its long journey to our earth? Does it change in the centuries, and even millions of years, of its course?

Here there arose an opportunity for various theories and for alternative interpretations of Hubble's results. How could possible changes in a ray of light along its path to the earth be measured, and with what accuracy? The most accurate linear measure we have depends on those rays of light. A metre, which for decades had been defined by the distance between two marks on a standard bar made of a precious metal, is now defined by 1,650,763·73 wavelengths of the light from a crypton lamp. The marks on the standard metre bar were too broad to allow really accurate measurement of the length of a metre. It was hardly possible to imagine a way of measuring changes in light, if light itself was the standard measure. Nevertheless, a solution of this problem was on the way.

Dr. Rudolf L. Mössbauer, the young German Nobel Prize winner for physics in 1961, established the basis of a method which makes possible measurement of such extreme accuracy as, for example, the determination of the effect of gravity on light rays. It is true that such measurements would be impossible with visible light. The Mössbauer effect belongs to the range of gamma-radiation of the atomic nucleus, a kind of light radiation of extremely short wavelength within the range of the electromagnetic spectrum ranging from long radio waves to high-altitude cosmic rays. Over a relatively short path in the laboratory this "light" radiation is changed by the earth's gravity to an extent which can be clearly recorded.

It is therefore not surprising that a large number of papers were soon published explaining the "fatigue" or "ageing" of light in the gravitational field of stars, particularly as Einstein had already deduced theoretically that light might be affected in this way. Experimental confirmation of this hypothesis had been expected in vain of many earlier experiments. As is usual in a sudden leap forward, basic principles are being re-examined. If radiation and gravity can be connected in theory, what are the laws governing them? If light is affected in outer space, if the energy of light decreases on the way, where does it go? Is there any connection between radiation and the generation of matter? Did creation start with a radiation field? This series of questions could be continued *ad lib*.

A Soviet scientist recently went to the extreme limit of postulating that:

1. The red shift in the terrestrial field and in outer space, as measured by Hubble, has the same cause, i.e., the effect of the gravitational field on photons (basic light units).
2. The universe is not expanding.

Before these statements can be accepted, certain phenomena require an explanation, and that may not be easy to find. On the other hand, it is quite possible that Hubble's expanding-universe theory will have to undergo modifications. It is frequently found that findings have to be re-examined after a few years, that they constitute a special case for which more precise, and more general, laws have to be determined. This may be such a case.

The question with which this book started was: When did it happen? When was the world created? This is a very popular question at the moment, but, scientifically speaking, it shows the wrong approach. The question should be, rather, when did creation start? Because it is obvious that creation is far from complete. We are contemporaries of the coming into existence of new stars, even whole new worlds. Even if the process takes millions of years, they are as nothing compared with eternity. We do not know whether creation will ever be complete. Perhaps the expansion of the universe will one day reach a maximum, and after that the universe will continue to exist in some final form. Perhaps it will then start to contract, to shrink, to die, and end in nothing.

We cannot see into the future, but we are now witnesses of creation on a much grander scale than that described to us in the Bible.

Is the Bible correct when it describes the creation of *one* world only? Have several worlds been created? Not even the biggest astronomical telescopes give any indication of the existence of other worlds. In the course of the past twenty years, however, a method has been developed which, although by no means technically perfected yet, gives indications of the possibility of another world beyond that so far investigated. This new method is radioastronomy.

CHAPTER 7

SEEING WHERE THERE IS NO LIGHT

Message from Jupiter. A day on Venus is ten days on earth.
Extra-terrestrial metals.

FOR thousands of years men have admired the bright stars of the night sky. There seems to be an "infinite" number of them, but if anybody seriously tried on a clear moonless night to count the stars visible to the naked eye he would hardly reach 2,000. Estimating the counting time as two seconds per star, he could finish his counting in an hour or so. The big telescope of the Mount Wilson Observatory in California makes 500 million stars visible to the observer. Counting them would take 226 years, provided one counted day and night without interruption.

Heinrich W. M. Olbers (1758–1840), a doctor and astronomer from Bremen, was thinking about something entirely different when he looked at the starry sky. He wondered why the sky looked so black in spite of the bright stars. He thought that if the stars were evenly distributed the sky would look like a luminous disk. Somewhere in the depths of cosmic space the eye would always find a star, and yet the night sky looks black even through the best telescope. There are, however, dark stars, and in some places clouds of dust which defy penetration by the eye. Besides, the stars are certainly not evenly distributed, but are grouped in the Milky Way. In Olbers's time the question of what exists where the sky is dark seemed unanswerable, for where there is no light we cannot see. And yet we are now beginning to discern another universe beyond the visible one.

In 1928 a discovery was made by accident. The American Bell Company operated a transatlantic radio-telephony network, but the latter did not work satisfactorily, there was much intermittent interference. To find the cause of the trouble, the firm asked a young physicist to examine the problem. The twenty-three-year-old Karl Jansky built a 48-foot aerial mounted on wheels and placed it on a circle of bricks, so that he could rotate it. He recorded the results of his investigations. Apart from technical troubles in the installation itself and the effects of thunderstorms and other interference, his report mentioned something entirely new: "Electromagnetic waves in the atmosphere, evidently coming from a certain direction in space" were contributing to the interference. Apparently, radio waves of some kind were reaching the earth from the Milky Way, ranging in length between some centimetres and several metres. Cosmic forces were interfering with radio transmission. Were extra-terrestrial creatures trying to communicate with us? Scientists took a more sober view of the discovery. They quickly ascertained that the waves emanated from specific regions. During the first years after the war it was demonstrated that the sun too sent out radio waves. Our neighbouring planet Jupiter emits particularly strong waves, which we are now capable of receiving. The majority of the radio waves, however, come from the gas clouds between the stars.

Message from Jupiter

Radioastronomy became established as a branch of science. The outsize aerial arrays which serve radioastronomers as telescopes were gradually improved. Today there exist dish-shaped movable aerials of enormous size. The largest radiotelescope at present is at Jodrell Bank near Manchester. This astral direction-finder has an aerial 250 feet in diameter, mounted on two 183-foot-high steel towers. Only five or six minutes are required for angular adjustments of the dish aerial.

There is a German radiotelescope on Mount Stockert near Bonn. Its aluminium aerial is $83\frac{1}{2}$ feet in diameter. An outsize radiotelescope, with an aerial dish of 643 feet, is at present under construction in the United States at an estimated cost of $79 million. There are also radiotelescopes with fixed aerials hundreds of yards long. The orientation of these installations towards localities in the universe has generally to be left to the rotation of the earth. An aerial array of this kind, 667 feet in length, is at Sydney, Australia. It is capable of picking out the waves emitted by a relatively small object, such as a sun spot. The Australian astronomers are particularly interested in radioastronomy and have another radiotelescope with two aerial arrays arranged at a distance of about $5\frac{1}{2}$ miles from each other.

Perhaps the most famous radioastronomical installation is a former German radar station located in the Netherlands. It is a "Würzburg giant" type direction-finding device which was used for the radar detection of distant bomber flights during the war. J. H. Oort and his colleagues at Kootwijk, near Apeldoorn, subsequently used it for the study of the distribution of matter in the Milky Way.

What is the source of this radiation from space? Hydrogen, which is distributed throughout the universe, accounts for a considerable amount of it, with a wavelength of 21 cm. Hydrogen is also of vital importance in the formation of new stars.

Locations in space where at some time a nova, a new star, had flared up were also shown to be sources of radiation. The star which in 1054 flared up so brilliantly that it was visible in daytime in spite of the sun has now turned into a gaseous cloud which emits radio waves, and the central star is now scarcely visible. The gaseous cloud is expanding at the incredible velocity of about 688 miles per second. In the constellation of Cassiopeia, the W star formation clearly observable in the night sky, a radio wave source was located first and later a weak, frayed-looking nebula which is possibly the remnant of a nova of A.D. 369. There is also a weak radio-wave source at the spot where Tycho Brahe observed a nova in 1572. Radio waves emanating from the constellation of Cygnus have also been detected. When the location of this radio source was examined with optical telescopes it became obvious that two galaxies intersected in this area, and the resultant disturbance may account for the observed radiation.

When the radio waves emanating from Jupiter were examined more closely strange phenomena were observed. The radiation is by no means uniform, and periodic outbursts take place. Sometimes these last only for a few seconds, at other times perhaps for an hour. The power of this radiation occasionally exceeds more than 200 times that of all other known cosmic radiation sources. Accurate measurements have shown that there are at least three radiation sources in Jupiter. The regularity of the emissions suggests that these sources are on the surface of the planet and not in the gaseous clouds surrounding it. Whether this opens up the possibility of determining the still unknown time of rotation of the planet, i.e., the length of a Jupiter day, is still an open question. First the cause of these periodic emissions will have to be established.

Because of the great variations in the radiation from Jupiter, it was first suspected that enormous electrical discharges, a kind of lightning, might be the cause of the radio waves. Today, however, it is thought more probable that the Jupiter radiation

74

depends on solar eruptions. It is also possible that Jupiter, like the earth, is surrounded by one or more radiation belts (Van Allen belts) which may affect the emitted radiation.

One day on Venus is ten days on earth

For many years astronomers argued whether our Milky Way rotated like a Catherine Wheel (or lawn sprinkler), i.e., whether the arms of the spiral nebula lagged behind the central part, or whether the motion was in the precisely opposite direction. Radioastronomy was able to prove that the motion was like that of a Catherine Wheel. The simpler idea proved once again to be correct. Two large spiral arms were discovered in the proximity of our Milky Way, and they rotated at a speed of over 125 miles per second.

Radioastronomy has proved to be an especially important method for the investigation of those areas in the sky which were formerly regarded as black or "empty". Radio waves reach us from outer space, but that is not the whole story. During the Second World War radar equipment successfully sent electromagnetic waves to the moon. A radar device was used to emit waves for a fraction of a second and then switched over to reception. In the meantime the transmitted waves had reached the moon, which reflected them, and on return to earth they were picked up by the aerial of the radar device. This process is similar to an echo, except that sound in the air travels at about 1,100 feet a second, while radar signals travel at 189,000 miles a second. In both cases the distance of the reflecting body from the transmitter can be established from the time difference between sending out a signal and getting it back. Indeed, the method works with extraordinary accuracy. Let us assume that an aircraft is 10 miles away. The passage of the wave there and back would involve a journey of 20 miles, which would take approximately one-ten-thousandth of a second. But by radar we can detect aircraft nearer than 10 miles with an accuracy of a few yards either way.

Not only was the distance of the moon from the earth measured anew by radar but also Venus was contacted by radar waves. The first radar contact with Venus was made on February 10th, 1958. On that day Venus was about 28 million miles away. The waves took five minutes to get there and back. Naturally, it was not a burst of music that was broadcast to Venus, but a brief sequence of pulses, and it was difficult to distinguish the signals among the flood of other noises from terrestrial sources. In view of the vast distance, the energy which Venus can reflect back to earth is very small, and only a fraction of it reaches the aerial of a radar device, no matter how large. Nevertheless, the experiment succeeded and when it was repeated two days later the distance between the earth and Venus had increased by a further 700,000 miles, so that the reflected pulses reached the earth 7·5 seconds later.

Even greater achievements became possible. Soviet radar measurements led to the conclusion that Venus takes ten terrestrial days to rotate round its axis, and therefore a Venusian day is 240 hours long by our reckoning. At the same time distances within our solar system were determined with greater precision by means of these measurements. The distance from the earth to the sun was established as 93,410,625 miles, with a margin of error of 3,125 miles.

After a successful reception, 650 miles from the transmitter, of a news broadcast reflected from the moon in 1951 the idea arose of using incoming meteorites for radio transmission. It is true that a very complex installation is required. First, the signals which are to be sent have to be stored electronically. Then an instrument is required which registers the appearance of a meteorite. As soon as a radar echo from a meteorite is recorded, the previously stored signal is transmitted. All this has to take place within one second, for a meteorite or its track cannot reflect signals over a long period. The signals are then decoded at the reception end. This method was proved to be applicable in the northern parts of Canada, where the normal short-wave radio is frequently distorted by atmospheric interference.

Extra-terrestrial metals

Radioastronomy is a young science. It is to be hoped that its methods will be improved and that sensitive aerial arrays will be developed which will not be merely bigger and more expensive. Unlike optical astronomy with its telescopes, radioastronomy has the advantage of being able to obtain information from areas of the universe so remote that the light which reaches us from them is too feeble to be recorded astronomically, even with the most sensitive instruments. This advantage is, however, still counterbalanced by the disadvantage that the range of wavelengths with which radioastronomy operates defies clear delimitation. Light from the stars can be analysed spectroscopically with great accuracy, and therefore the proof of the Doppler effect detected by Hubble was clear and accurate. In radioastronomy the only available spectroscopic line for a similar test is the 21-cm hydrogen line, and this is comparatively feeble. Consequently, there is a big margin of error in very distant objects. The waves which reach us are much more difficult to focus than the light waves used in optical astronomy. In order to minimise these difficulties as much as possible the orbital movement of the moon has been utilised. As it passes the moon cuts off some of the wave transmissions. If a radio-telescope is made to follow the moon's trailing rim a cosmic radio source can be observed at the moment when its radiation is no longer impeded by the moon.

Radioastronomy has yet another disadvantage compared with optical astronomy. The spectra of stars show incontrovertibly what chemical elements are present, particularly if they are elements which also occur on earth. However, many chemical reactions take place in the depths of the universe which are not known on earth. It would take us too far afield to discuss here the chemical composition of the stars, no matter how interesting it would be to discuss red giants, for instance, which are enormous formations of low density, or white dwarfs, relatively small structures of very high temperature. The red giants contain extremely large amounts of well-known heavy chemical elements. Some red giants also show spectral lines of the element technetium. As its name indicates, on earth this is an artificial element. It was obtained a few years ago in very small quantities during nuclear transformations. Measured by cosmic standards, it decays so fast that we cannot hope to obtain it in measurable quantities.

The loss of brightness of young novae after their explosion shows in some cases the presence of the chemical element californium, an isotope with a half-life of 55 days. Like technetium, californium, which is a so-called transuranic element, does not occur naturally on earth. Minute amounts of it have been obtained artificially, using the most modern equipment of nuclear physics.

The long-held assumption that nuclear chemical reactions which release vast amounts of energy take place in the stars was first demonstrated in regard to the sun. In processes similar to those of the hydrogen bomb, hydrogen atoms are fused into

77

helium atoms (four hydrogen atoms into one helium atom), with the release of huge quantities of energy.

In 1938 details and intermediate stages of this reaction were explained, and calculations led to the comforting conclusion that the sun had so far used up only 8 per cent of its hydrogen content. The possible annihilation of life on earth by freezing is therefore a matter for the very remote future. On the other hand, it is rather remarkable to realise that we, who depend on the sun for our life, have been living on atomic energy from the beginning of time.

To summarise, then, we see that the universe contains matter similar in structure to that familiar on earth. Where did this matter come from for the act of creation?

CHAPTER 8

RAW MATERIAL OF A WORLD

Bikini, the hydrogen bomb and the sun. The formation of elements. Mass and gravity.

IN July, 1946, a small group of German physicists met at Mosbach, Baden. This was not a happy meeting, it was a stocktaking of ruins which had survived the war. The small, neat, medieval town was a good setting for it. Nobody knew how scientific research could be carried on. Several fields of research had become forbidden territory, many scientific colleagues were dead or missing, in exile, jobless, or without resources. Was there any point in starting up German scientific research again? On July 1st the first post-war atomic bomb had been exploded, and work on new and more terrible means of mass destruction was being diligently carried on. The first big atomic underwater explosion was planned at Bikini for July 25th.

Pascual Jordan was among those who came to Mosbach. He and the other physicists had spent much time discussing the American atomic tests. Like most of his colleagues, he intended to leave on the morning after the meeting was over, but on July 24th an acquaintance found him still there, relaxing peacefully in a meadow.

"Still here, Herr Jordan! Weren't you going to leave a few days ago?"

"I changed my mind," said Jordan. "I'm waiting till tomorrow. Tomorrow they are having the underwater test. If our colleague Bethe happens to have made a slight miscalculation the whole world may blow up. In the meantime it doesn't seem worth while undertaking a strenuous journey."

He was not the only physicist who was worried. Nobody knew what would happen when a nuclear bomb was exploded under water. It might start a nuclear reaction. Every molecule of water contains two atoms of hydrogen. The latter might be transformed into helium and turn the nuclear test into an outsize hydrogen-bomb explosion which would destroy the earth.

Today we know this to be impossible, but at the time there was much ignorance, even in the United States, about what would happen, though this did not become apparent until later. There was no intention of sacrificing in the experiment the Bikini naval task force, including the still effective warships *Nevada* (United States), *Negato* (Japan), *Prinz Eugen* (German cruiser) and *Saratoga* (United States aircraft carrier), as well as dozens of smaller vessels. However, the vessels which did not perish in the explosion were so contaminated with radioactivity that they had to be left at Bikini for about ten years before they could be broken up. Nobody had expected that.

The processes which take place in an exploding hydrogen bomb are similar to those occurring in the sun. These processes have been investigated and explained by Carl Friedrich von Weizsäcker and Hans Bethe, the research physicist mentioned by Jordan. Bethe is the son of a well-known German physiologist. He emigrated in 1933, and won much support, as well as much disapproval, in the United States, by his opposition to the development of the hydrogen bomb.

The processes taking place in the sun are a complicated sequence of six reaction stages which result in the fusion of hydrogen nuclei to form helium in a quadruple cyclic reaction. This process releases enough energy to keep the sun at its usual temperature of about 20 million degrees Centigrade (36 million degrees Fahrenheit) in the reaction areas. The nuclei of carbon, nitrogen and oxygen have certain catalytic functions in this process, they act as a conveyor belt, as it were, in the building up of the helium atom.

Bethe was able to show that the available astrophysical data confirm the various phases of this process. Even if some corrections may become necessary, the basic concepts of this theory are not likely to undergo changes. The solar processes can be applied to other luminescent stars without occasioning much error. Some stars are brighter than our sun, and the explanation is simply that the basic reaction is faster, for the mass of these stars is invariably greater than that of the sun.

Where do the materials come from which the sun uses for hydrogen fusion, and where do some stars get chemical elements such as technetium and californium? Pascual Jordan postulated the creation of the universe from two elementary particles. Even if we assume the addition of positive and negative charges, and possibly, too, the formation of hydrogen, does that give us

Arctic night in Northern Finland, winter 1959–60

The Queen Maud Mountain Range in the Antarctic

Manganese nuggets on red clay at a depth of 16,000 ft. No sign of living creatures, presumably the current is not strong enough. The photograph covers about 20 square feet

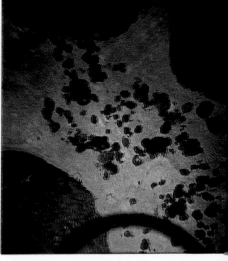

Ocean bed in the South-Western Pacific, showing manganese nuggets of various sizes on chalk silt, at a depth of over 15,000 feet. Traces of the passage of worm-like marine creatures can be seen. The photograph covers about square feet

the answer to the origin of, for instance, the iron which is floating about in cosmic space in the form of meteors?

The formation of elements

What is the origin of chemical elements? The simplest reply is in another question: Why should we assume that they originated? It is said that they were created by God.

Such a reply precludes any discussion, and does not do justice either to the nature of creation or to its grandeur. Let us return to the question and treat it as a basis for discussion, starting with what we can observe on earth. Heavy elements, such as uranium and radium, disintegrate into smaller units. Much thought has been devoted to the possibility that the heavy elements were created first, perhaps a super-heavy element such as californium. If we assume that about 5,000 million years ago all matter was of extreme density, and formed a kind of primeval egg, we can explain some of the facts.

However, this concept is not particularly enlightening or useful. Even if we deliberately start with an ill-defined blob of primeval matter in order to avoid the concept of an "element", we are still faced with a difficulty. Before there was a blob there must have been *half* a blob of matter which began to decay. It is not easy to imagine anything that was just an undefined blob of something decaying into definite types of particles. At least, that is how a physicist would see the problem. No doubt it is easier to start with the idea of one or several primeval components which formed more highly organised units at a later stage. Pascual Jordan's assumption is not based on a mathematically proved, logical train of thought, it simply tallies with the common-sense idea that complicated things can be built up from simple ones.

Let us consider the possibility of the building up of elements. First, neutrons, i.e., particles without a charge, are assumed to have been formed, and some of them became hydrogen nuclei. Later, other nuclei of higher elements were formed, etc. On this assumption the elements with the largest, heaviest nuclei of complicated structure would be the last to be formed. If we adopt this view we shall find it easy to explain the fact that the higher the atomic weight of an element, the rarer it is. The early part of the periodic table of elements consists mostly of elements whose atomic weight can be divided by four. One could well imagine that helium, which has a mass of 4, and

F
81

which we know from hydrogen-bomb and solar research as an end-product poor in energy, could serve as a basic unit. As we know, creation is not yet complete, and therefore we should be able to observe these processes in operation. Consequently, we must examine the "private lives" of stars in detail. The word "life" in regard to a star is quite justified.

As soon as the stellar material has accumulated and agglomerated into a mass, either through a vortex effect or through the force of gravity, the hydrogen "burns up" and forms helium (mass 4). When a considerable volume of the original gas is used up a contraction follows, raising the temperature of the mass to about 100 million degrees Centigrade while, via an intermediate stage, beryllium (8) and carbon (12) are formed. The bracketed mass numbers indicate that the development of the star has reached the stage where the predominant elements that originate are those whose mass numbers are divisible by four. In addition, neutrons (mass 1) are released during these processes, and it is these neutrons which ensure the subsequent creation of elements with odd, and increasingly higher, mass numbers.

Many of these processes are still barely understood. However, creative reactions during which iron is found to originate can be accounted for without auxiliary hypotheses. In the same way the formation of elements up to uranium can take place during a certain developmental stage of a star. If this is so, an initial formation of relatively large amounts of californium should have taken place, and this corresponds to our observations. The occurrence of novae and supernovae supplement the picture. They are by no means inexplicable exceptions.

A more complete understanding may be achieved by mentioning the stars which have used up their available energy. They remain dark and dead in cosmic space.

Mass and gravity

While we arrive in this way at a number of concepts which are more or less confirmed by quantitative estimates, we are still left with the question of the origin of the initial two particles. If the origin of these two primary particles is really the start of a creation which is still in progress, how are we to explain the expansion of the universe, and how can new stellar matter continue to be formed? These postulates still leave us without a satisfactory answer.

Let us consider the second group of problems first. Expansion can be explained by the assumption of a continuous reduction in gravity. Everywhere in the universe we observe orbital motion caused by the force of gravity. The orbit of the earth round the sun is mainly determined by the mutual forces of attraction between the earth and the sun. A rocket circling the earth moves along a curve determined by the force of gravity, i.e., its attraction by the earth. If we assume, therefore, that this force is decreasing at such a slow rate that we cannot measure it the constituents of our universe are bound to recede from each other. This, then, is a possible explanation of the expanding universe.

This explanation inevitably raises a further question. If the force that holds the world together is decreasing it cannot simply dwindle, it is bound to appear elsewhere in the universe in another form. All hypotheses are suspect if they go against the basic law of nature that the total sum of matter and energy is constant.

In order to solve this dilemma, we could assume that the loss in gravitation energy appears elsewhere in the universe in the form of matter. This is a very tempting idea, for it would help us to understand how new stars are formed. However, we are unable to prove it.

In the last few years, however, there has arisen a theory, as yet no more than a vague hypothesis, which may sweep aside all previous attempts to explain these problems. Moreover, it is not in contradiction with Pascual Jordan's idea of two elementary particles if we assume, instead of two neutrons, two primary particles with opposite electrical charges.

CHAPTER 9

ANTI-MATTER AND ANTI-UNIVERSE

The gaps in the periodic system are filling in. Synthetic
elements. Did God create anti-matter as well? The case of
the apple falling upwards.

IF you ask a chemist what chemistry is, he generally hesitates.
On the spur of the moment it is almost as difficult to give a
layman a comprehensible and unequivocal definition of a
science as it is to describe a spiral staircase without using one's
hands.

In both cases the subject requires visual experience in order
to be understood. That was probably the idea behind the
publication, by Professor Friedrich Runge, in 1846, of the
strangest chemistry book ever written. The few existing copies
are rarities in antiquarian bookshops. Its title page bears the
inscription: "Published by the Association for the Dissemina-
tion of Useful Knowledge by Comprehensible Publications.
Patron: H.R.H. Crown Prince Maximilian of Bavaria." The
two volumes of this work contain, on carefully glued-in strips
of paper, samples of the chemicals discussed in the adjoining
pages. Skimming through the pages reveals a whole gamut of
colours: white, yellow, red, orange, black, green and many
others.

Runge, famous as the discoverer of aniline in coal tar, but
unfortunately almost completely unknown to the housewife as
an eager advocate of tinned foods, was determined to make himself understood. He had obviously cogitated at great length
before he wrote the first sentences of the book:

"Chemistry is the science of the components of our earth.
"Everything around us, whether resting, moving or standing, is the subject of chemical research: air and water, metals
and minerals, plants and animals, all come within the scope
of chemistry."

That is surely a clear and comprehensible definition.
Since Runge's time chemistry has changed considerably, but

the century-old definition, "the science of the components of our earth", has not been invalidated.

Our earth is said to be composed of ninty-two basic substances which the chemists call elements. During the past few years nuclear physicists have added some artificial elements to the list. These new elements revealed no surprises as regards their structure, and they are without importance in our lives, unless the latter should be terminated by an explosion of a plutonium (element 94) bomb.

Chemists combine these ninety-two elements into most astounding compounds. Frequently these compounds are substances which did not previously exist in nature. The smallest, chemically indivisible particle of an element which the chemist can separate from one substance and build into another is called an atom, the Greek word for "indivisible". For a long time chemists were rather proud of their indivisible atom. Today every newspaper reader knows that the atom has no right to its name, because it is divisible. Nuclear fission and nuclear power have become everyday concepts.

The gaps in the periodic system are filling in

Why are there just these ninety-two elements? Not all of them were discovered at the same time. Let us disregard the theories of the ancients, who imagined all substances to be derived from earth, water, air and fire, which they called elements, and let us look at the chemical elements we know, such as gold, silver, copper, iron, hydrogen, oxygen, arsenic and sulphur. The famous French chemist Lavoisier, who was guillotined during the French Revolution, knew only about twenty elements. About 1800 thirty-four elements were known, and twenty years later forty-six. At the time of the 1870 war chemists had knowledge of sixty elements. By 1914 it was known that there must be ninety-two, though only eighty-six had been discovered. At the beginning of the Second World War in 1939 doubts arose about ninety-two being the maximum number of elements. It was not expected, however, that more than ninety-two would be found in a natural state on earth.

The reason was simple. When a considerable number of elements had become known, attempts were made to arrange them into some kind of order. Professor Wolfgang Döbereiner of Jena, who shared a taste for natural science with his

Elements Known in 1800

(arranged in the order of the modern periodic system)

	1	2	3	4	5	6	7	8
I	1 Hydrogen							
II		4 Beryllium	5 Boron	6 Carbon	7 Nitrogen	8 Oxygen		
III		12 Magnesium			15 Phosphorus	16 Sulphur	17 Chlorine	
IV	29 Copper	30 Zinc		22 Titanium	33 Arsenic	24 Chromium	25 Manganese	26 Iron 27 Cobalt 28 Nickel
V	47 Silver	38 Strontium	39 Yttrium	40 Zirconium 50 Tin	51 Antimony	52 Tellurium		
VI	79 Gold	56 Barium 80 Mercury		82 Lead	83 Bismuth	74 Tungsten		78 Platinum
VII						92 Uranium		

Periodic System of Elements in 1962

	1	2	3	4	5	6	7	8
I	1 Hydrogen							2 Helium
II	3 Lithium	4 Beryllium	5 Boron	6 Carbon	7 Nitrogen	8 Oxygen	9 Fluorine	10 Neon
III	11 Sodium	12 Magnesium	13 Aluminium	14 Silicon	15 Phosphorus	16 Sulphur	17 Chlorine	18 Argon
IV	19 Potassium	20 Calcium	21* Scandium	22 Titanium	23 Vanadium	24 Chromium	25 Manganese	26 Iron 27 Cobalt 28 Nickel
	29 Copper	30 Zinc	31* Gallium	32* Germanium	33 Arsenic	34 Selenium	35 Bromine	36 Crypton
V	37 Rubidium	38 Strontium	39 Yttrium	40 Zirconium	41 Niobium	42 Molybdenum	43 Technetium	44 Ruthenium 45 Rhodium 46 Palladium
	47 Silver	48 Cadmium	49 Indium	50 Tin	51 Antimony	52 Tellurium	53 Iodine	54 Xenon
VI	55 Caesium	56 Barium	57–71 Rare Earths	72 Hafnium	73 Tantalum	74 Tungsten	75 Rhenium	76 Osmium 77 Iridium 78 Platinum
	79 Gold	80 Mercury	81 Thallium	82 Lead	83 Bismuth	84 Polonium	85 Astatinium	86 Radon
VII	87 Francium	88 Radium	89 Actinium	90 Thorium	91 Protactinium	92 Uranium		

Rare Earths	57 Lanthanum	58 Cerium	59 Praseodymium	60 Neodymium	61 Promethium	62 Samarium	63 Europium	64 Gadolinium	65 Terbium	66 Dysprosium	67 Holmium	68 Erbium	69 Thulium	70 Ytterbium	71 Lutetium

Artificially produced transuranic elements	93 Neptunium	94 Plutonium	95 Americium	96 Curium	97 Berkelium	98 Californium	99 Einsteinium	100 Fermium	101 Mendelevium	102 Nobelium	103 Lawrencium

* Elements predicted by Mendeleyev.

contemporary and namesake, the poet Wolfgang von Goethe, tried to arrange the elements into some comprehensive system. It is, of course, possible to arrange things on the barrack-square principle of "tall at one end, short at the other", but such a system would be of little use in chemistry. About 1870, almost simultaneously, Mendeleyev, a Russian, and Lothar Meyer, a German, arranged the elements in an order which made sense chemically. They both developed the well-known periodic system of elements, usually referred to simply as the periodic system. This still enjoys general favour. In the course of recent decades new and "improved" versions have been put forward, but nearly all of them are considerably less convenient than the original version.

About 1914 it became clear that this excellent system had one fault: it was not absolutely correct, it was accurate only if gaps were left here and there. These gaps, however, as Lothar Meyer had already found out, meant only that certain elements were still unknown, had not yet been discovered. The periodic system proved an excellent guide for searching for them. All one had to do was to see what qualities the neighbouring elements had and in what minerals they could be found. After that it was easy to estimate what the missing element should be like, and where it might be found. This approach to the "element chase" has proved the right one. Gradually all the elements have been fitted into the system, right up to uranium, which had the serial number of 92. Element 43, which is now called technetium, and had been shown to exist outside the earth, could not be found on earth. At one time it was believed to have been discovered, and the discoverers immediately called their find "masurium", but it proved a false alarm. Ultimately the first visible amounts of the element, a silvery white powder, were obtained in the United States during nuclear-reactor experiments. Astatinium is another element that can be obtained on earth only by nuclear chemistry processes. It is chemically related to iodine, bromine, chlorine and fluorine, which are above it in the periodic table.

The reason for believing that there were only ninety-two elements was apparently based on the structure of the periodic system, which, starting with hydrogen and ending with uranium, had room for only ninety-two elements. However, that is not an adequate reason. A look at the structure of elements may be more enlightening. Let us start at the lower

end of the periodic system and examine the atomic structure of
hydrogen, helium and lithium.

Element	Hydrogen	Helium	Lithium
Positive charge in the nucleus	1	2	3
Mass	1	4	7

The hydrogen atom has the simplest structure of all atoms.
In the centre it has a very small but relatively heavy nucleus
which has a positive electrical charge and is called a proton.
Round it circles an electron, an electrically negative charge
unit, and the two charges balance each other out.

The atomic nucleus of helium contains two positively charged
elementary particles (protons) and two neutral elementary
particles (neutrons), as well as two electrons which orbit round
the nucleus and balance the charge. The atomic nucleus of
lithium consists of three protons, and has therefore a triple
positive charge, as well as four neutrons. Three electrons circle
round it. And so the series of elements continues up to element
92, which has ninety-two positively charged nuclear particles
and ninety-two electrons round it. The number of neutral
particles in the nucleus rises more irregularly along the periodic
table, and chemistry text-books publish complicated tables
about their sequence.

Starting with hydrogen, the nucleus of which has only one
positive charge, there is an uninterrupted series of elements,
each higher than the preceding one, up to uranium, the element
with ninety-two positive charges. When chemists want to be
quite accurate they include the number of positive charges,
called the atomic number, in the designation of an element, e.g.,
uranium-238 is written as:

$$_{92}^{238}U$$

Then one can see at a glance that:

(1) the element is uranium;

(2) the nucleus contains 92 positive charges (protons),
92 is its atomic number;

(3) the mass number of the substance in question is 238.

Synthetic elements

Although uranium is the element with the highest positive
nuclear charge encountered in nature, there is no irrefutable
reason for supposing that the table of elements comes to an end

with uranium. Today we know that there actually exist several transuranic elements. Some of them have been produced artificially by the pound. Their names and atomic numbers are:

Neptunium	93
Plutonium	94
Americium	95
Curium	96
Berkelium	97
Californium	98
Einsteinium	99
Fermium	100
Mendelevium	101
Nobelium	102
Lawrencium	103

Admittedly, up to now only a few atoms of the last few elements have been recorded by means of highly sensitive instruments. Nobody has yet seen them in bulk.

The synthetic element plutonium is usually the starting material for producing further transuranic elements. The difficulties of this type of work may be judged by the fact that a plutonium–aluminium alloy has been irradiated in an atomic reactor for six years in order to obtain from it, by chemical separation: 200 mg curium-244, 75 mg americium-234 (1 mg equals $\frac{4}{100,000}$ oz), as well as even smaller amounts of berkelium and californium. After two years of irradiating a rod containing 78 g (less than 3 oz) of plutonium, 1 g of americium-243, $\frac{1}{2}$ g of curium-244 and 6 g of plutonium-242 were obtained. Plutonium-242 is at present the most important basic material for the production of transuranic elements. The discovery of elements of an even higher positive-charge or atomic number than lawrencium (103) may be expected.

Further elements can be added to the high-atomic-number end of the periodic system, but can anything be done about the lower end?

The decisive point is apparently the positive charge of the atomic nucleus. If we could take away the only positive charge or proton of heavy hydrogen we would be left with a neutron. The neutron still has a mass of 1 and could be called a chemical element without a charge, and many scientists do so and write the periodic system as:

Neutron/Hydrogen/Helium/Lithium/Beryllium/etc.

Atomic number   0   1   2   3   4

What would remain if the mass 1 of the neutron was taken away? Nothing. That may sound absurd, but it is not really. In order to explain some of their observations, nuclear physicists found that they had to include a kind of "no-thing" in their calculations. This "no-thing" has been named a neutrino. We shall not discuss this particle in detail here, but only mention that, in principle, consideration of a "no-thing" is not as new an idea as it might at first appear. Mendeleyev, the imaginative genius who was one of the last universal natural scientists, had been far too fond of analogies to miss an idea of this nature. He added the element "coronium" to precede hydrogen in the periodic table. He believed that it came from the sun. We know now that the neutron which we are inserting before hydrogen actually occurs on the sun.

Moreover, Mendeleyev concluded that there must be a particle with an atomic weight of: $\dfrac{3 \cdot 5}{100,000,000,000}$ (i.e., $3 \cdot 5 \cdot 10^{-11}$). He assumed that it was the "ether" which the physicists of that time postulated, and, as a token of his profound admiration for Isaac Newton, the great British physicist, he called it "newtonium". We do not know of a particle which corresponds exactly to Mendeleyev's newtonium, but perhaps we can class it as an extraordinarily good approximation to the above-mentioned neutrino.

For a long time it seemed that the series of elements did not extend beyond the initial beginning of the periodic table. However, the start of a new development in thought which ultimately led to the revolutionary concept of anti-matter lay there.

Did God create anti-matter as well?

Emilio G. Segrè, a scientist who originally showed no interest in this complex set of problems at all, became the king-pin of anti-matter research.

In 1925–26 he was studying engineering in Rome and came into contact with Enrico Fermi, the nuclear physicist, and his group of scientists. In September, 1927, all of them went to Como together, firstly, because it is a lovely place anyway, and secondly, because they were all anxious to take a look at the famous nuclear physicists who were then in Como for a nuclear-physics conference.

"Who is the man with the gentle look and the indistinct pro-nunciation?" Segrè asked his companions.

"That is Bohr."

"Bohr? Who is he?"

"Would you believe it! Have you never heard of Bohr's atomic model?"

"No. Tell me."

Segrè was told, and soon he began to take an interest in physics. In a very short time the twenty-two-year-old student became a member of Fermi's team. A year later Segrè took his degree in Rome, and his articles began to appear in scientific journals. He was present when the first neutron experiment was carried out in the goldfish pond of the Institute's Director. It was the classical experiment showing the effect of slowed-down neutrons. This pond, as Fermi explained, constituted the only convenient expanse of water readily available at the time. Soon afterwards Segrè became Professor of Physics and Director of the Physics Institute of Palermo University. He filled one of the gaps in the periodic system by discovering the artificial element technetium. His work was interrupted for a brief period when he had to emigrate to America in 1938. It was his research in the United States which led him to the idea of anti-matter.

If we leave the mass of atoms unchanged there is obviously only one way in which their nature can be changed, and that is by changing their electrical charge. In matter as we know it the atomic nucleus is positively charged. If the nucleus were charged negatively the charged particles orbiting around it would have to be positive. As we know of the existence of positrons and electrons, i.e., positive and negative charge units, we could easily imagine a reversal of this order. In fact, physicists have succeeded in producing atoms in which the charges actually were reversed in this manner.

We are able to create sporadic particles of anti-matter, but only by having large and complicated equipment: cyclotrons, magnetic fields, etc. The mass remains one, but the charge of the nucleus is negative.

Charge	+1	0	−1
Designation	Hydrogen	Neutron	Anti-hydrogen
Mass	1	1	1

As this experiment deals with elementary particles which

have no surrounding shell of electrons, i.e., "naked" atomic nuclei, we should, strictly speaking, call them "proton" and "anti-proton" instead of "hydrogen" and "anti-hydrogen", but the designation used above is more comprehensible. It leads us straight to the next question: Would it be possible to develop a whole periodic system of anti-elements? Is there any likelihood of having anti-matter compounds? Is there perhaps an entire "anti-world" built up of anti-particles?

We see with consternation that the exploration of an anti-world is closer at hand than many people believed. All that we need in the anti-world is the opposite of a neutron. Actually an anti-neutron has recently been observed. It was produced in an unorthodox manner, but the result cannot be doubted. In a simplified way the transformation equation would be: proton + anti-proton result in neutron + anti-neutron.

We may therefore at least imagine the outline of another world of elements. Anti-heavy hydrogen or anti-deuterium would consist of a nucleus containing an anti-proton plus an anti-neutron. Instead of an electron, there would be a positron orbiting around the nucleus. Correspondingly, anti-helium should consist of two anti-protons + two anti-neutrons, with two positrons in orbit around it. The anti-matter periodic system of elements can be built up further on the principle of every subsequent anti-element having one more negative charge in the nucleus and one more positron orbiting around it.

If we set out the relation in the form of a table, we get:

	World			Anti-world		
	Negative shell charge	Positive nucleus charge	Mass	Mass	Negative nucleus charge	Positive shell charge
Helium	2	2	4			
Deuterium	1	1	2			
Hydrogen	1	1	1			
Proton		1	1			
Neutron			1			
Anti-neutron				1		
Anti-proton				1	1	
Anti-hydrogen				1	1	1
Anti-deuterium				2	1	1
Anti-helium				4	2	2

What else do we know today about anti-matter? In view of its symmetrical structure we are able, as happened in regard to the original periodic system, to predict its properties fairly accurately. Undoubtedly it is as stable as ordinary matter, as long as it does not come into contact with the latter. If, however, considerable quantities of matter and anti-matter should meet, they would annihilate each other, and the concomitant release of energy would be such as to make an atomic-bomb explosion appear a harmless firework display.

Therefore no anti-matter can appear permanently on earth, and we cannot expect to find a deposit of anti-matter on it. Even single higher atoms of it are beyond the realms of possibility. Chemists need not worry about having to study anti-matter chemistry.

Nevertheless, we would do well not to thrust aside the idea that somewhere in cosmic space there might be considerable masses of anti-matter. In view of Nature's almost boring love of symmetry, the point is scarcely debatable. There is no proof as yet of anti-worlds or an anti-universe. Here on earth we can distinguish between hydrogen and anti-hydrogen, but in cosmic space this would be more difficult. Estimates showed that our galaxy has scarcely more than one anti-atomic nucleus per ten million normal atomic nuclei. However, scientists consider it conceivable that other ratios exist in other galaxies. The radiation of Cygnus A and Messier 87, which are outside our galaxy, may well be connected with the annihilation of anti-matter. At least some astronomers believe that the possibility cannot be excluded.

Will the whole world, as we know it, disappear one day, because, as in an equation, positive and negative will cancel each other out and nothing will remain? There is nothing basically new in this idea. It has been discussed often enough, and it can, of course, neither be proved nor disproved.

Emilio G. Segrè, Nobel Prize winner, described the situation recently in the words: "Suppose God has created the world, as you believe he did, is there any reason to assume that he preferred matter to anti-matter?"

The case of the apple falling upwards

Let us revert to the beginning of creation. We saw that perfect symmetry exists between particles and anti-particles. Why, and this is a perfectly legitimate question, why should matter

94

and anti-matter not have been created simultaneously? Every physics textbook deals with a case which might serve us as a metaphor: a beam of energy, an electromagnetic wave, can be converted into two particles of matter with opposite electrical charges, one of them positive, the other negative. Did creation start with a similar process?

C. J. Kevane, a physicist of Arizona University, published a theory of creation which includes anti-matter. His theory has not been examined in detail, but some ideas in it sound attractive. According to him, matter and anti-matter were united at the moment of creation, and their separation followed later, because between them were the mutually repellant forces of gravity and anti-gravity. The idea of anti-gravity is so new that it will take much effort to see whether it fits into our present image of the world. But C. J. Kevane is not alone in his belief in such a force.

George Gamow, the well-known American physicist of Russian origin, has expressed similar views. He started out with the assertion that it has not yet been proved experimentally whether anti-particles have a mass which can be considered positive from the gravitational aspect. If their "mass" is negative an "anti-apple" would fall upward!

This would result in a completely novel view of the world. In fact, we could hardly speak about *one* world, but until we have invented a new word for the duality of the forms of matter we shall have to continue to refer to two worlds.

The next few years will show whether the concepts of world and anti-world can be developed, and whether experimental data can be found or evolved to support them. A new idea like this will meet resistance and opposition, and will cause bitter controversy. However, we must not be narrow-minded, but be prepared to accept the apparent contradictions in order to explore the wide horizons which the new concept opens up.

If a new model image of the universe can be built up which includes the idea of anti-matter, and which may clear up some of the existing difficulties, it would not only constitute a scientific triumph, it would force us into facing anew the problem of man's relation to a greatly enlarged concept of the universe. We are inclined to treat the terms "earth" and "world" as interchangeable. Most of the time we forget that our entire solar system is only a minute part of one galaxy, and that even our galaxy is merely one cosmic entity among millions of others. If there is an anti-universe our "world" goes down another stage in the scale of importance. We must then revise the importance of our existence again, just as the contemporaries of Copernicus and Kepler had to do. We shall find it difficult for no other reason than the excessive sense of our own importance.

Volcanic activities which even today influence the shape of the earth include geysers and continuous steam eruptions. The photograph shows the Namaskard geysers in Iceland, which is an island of volcanic origin

The Poas volcano in Costa Rica, nearly 8,600 feet high. Its most recent eruption was in 1952, but minor volcanic activity in the form of steam and gas eruptions in the crater is continuous

CHAPTER 10

THE TINIEST PARTICLES

*Mesons and anti-mesons. Heisenberg's "world" formula.
What we see is the past.*

THE terms "universe" and "anti-universe" still sound strange
to us, but physicists glibly use and discuss them. Armed with
paper, pencil and the usual mathematical gadgets, scientists are
seeking ways of achieving a unified view of the world. They
seem quite unconcerned about whether their picture of the
universe is intelligible or not. Albert Einstein's wife described
the situation aptly when a colleague of her husband's once
showed her the cyclotron, weighing several hundred tons, with
which he worked. She asked why this enormous and very
expensive equipment was necessary, and was told that he used
it to examine the properties of elementary particles from which
he deduced the origin of the universe. "I don't understand,"
she exclaimed, "All my husband seems to need for that, when
he is at home in the evening, is a pencil and the back of an old
envelope."

In order to study physicists in their natural environment and
hear them talk about their work we should attend one of their
conferences, e.g., the Physics Section of the Nobel Prize winners'
Conference at Lindau on Lake Constance. Every year scientists
whose names have become world famous gather here, chemists
one year, physicists another, medical prize-winners a third and
so on.

There is a strange magic about those meetings in the delight-
ful old town. About the year 1230 the Discalced Carmelite
monks came to Lindau, and by 1270 they had built a monastery
and a church which later became, in turn, a prison, a barracks
and an armoury. Today it houses the municipal theatre, but for
one week in the year Nobel Prize winners take it over. Famous
scientists from all over the world walk through Lindau's medieval
streets, mixing with university rectors, deans and professors.
The Nobel Prize winners freely discuss opinions, ideas and
notions with students in inns and cafés, and on street corners.
There is an atmosphere of a family gathering of scientists.

G

On the eve of one of the physicists' meetings Hideki Yukawa, the Japanese physicist, was asked about the subject of his paper on the following day. The title was printed in the programme: "Attempts at Forming a Uniform Theory of Elementary Particles", but the actual contents were still under consideration, for, as Yukawa airily said, "I shall have to work out a few more equations before tomorrow." And when tomorrow came, his theories proved so new and bold that only a few of those present were able to follow. However, they all listened with rapt attention, spell-bound by the mode of thinking and the penetrating intellect of this remarkable scientist.

Professor C. F. Powell of Bristol was the next speaker. His subject was related to that of Yukawa's paper, but his presentation was clear, comprehensible and down to earth. "The main thing we want is a stratosphere balloon which can rise to an altitude of 20 miles, a fighter aircraft and a man-of-war or, well, a destroyer would do." What did he want them for? Let us examine Powell's researches in detail.

Mesons and anti-mesons

For a long time physicists were puzzled, on the one hand, by the causes of stability of ordinary atomic nuclei, and, on the other, by the cause of the decay of radioactive atomic nuclei. Why is the positive charge of a proton exactly the same as the negative charge of an electron? Why has the ratio of the mass of an electron and the mass of a proton the peculiar value of 1 to 1,837? What is the arrangement of the interior of an atomic nucleus? Questions were piling on questions. Yukawa's theory about the unknown forces of attraction within the nucleus merely raised another problem for the nuclear physicists, because Yukawa postulated a further elementary particle, a kind of atomic glue, whose mass was supposed to be several hundred times that of the electron.

Surprisingly enough, it was not very difficult to determine the existence of these new particles, later called "mesons". Two American physicists discovered particles which approximately corresponded to Yukawa's theoretical prognostications. However, there were still two obstacles to the exact measurement of these particles, and they were the reasons for Powell's surprising demand for the military equipment which he considered essential for his experiments. Mesons exist for a mere millionth of a second, and their observation presented a special problem.

Moreover, these particles originate only when very fast, i.e., high-energy, protons collide with atomic nuclei. To be sure, protons could be accelerated to the necessary speed in powerful cyclotrons, but there is an easier way of obtaining them. Protons occur in the natural high-altitude cosmic radiation with much higher energies than can be given to them artificially on earth. At an altitude of about 20 miles above the earth there are atoms with which the protons could collide, and therefore it could be assumed that mesons, too, are generated there. That still left scientists with the problem of recording the mesons. The proposed solution lay in obtaining the track of a passing meson on a photographic plate.

Powell's experimental technique consisted, in principle, of sending up a stack of suitable photographic plates to an altitude of about 20 miles in a balloon, and developing them when they landed. Whenever high-energy protons hit the atomic nuclei of the photographic emulsion mesons could be expected to show up.

The problem consisted in bringing the balloon down in a suitable area and recovering the exposed plates. If the balloon and the plates came down in an almost inaccessible area they were likely to be spoiled before they could be recovered. Powell decided that the plates should come down in the sea, from which they must be rescued with the utmost speed. He sent his first balloon up from Sardinia, and its flight was tracked by radar. As soon as the balloon began to lose height an aircraft was dispatched to the likely place of its descent. When the aircraft spotted the drifting balloon in the sea it summoned a destroyer to recover the plates.

Powell's method worked, though he encountered a few unexpected difficulties, e.g., when the skipper of a local fishing-boat found a balloon before the destroyer arrived on the spot, annexed the balloon envelope and ropes as salvage, but hastily threw the box of photographic plates overboard, as he suspected it of being a kind of bomb.

When the results of Powell's balloon flights came to be examined they were far from being clear-cut. The experimenters found not only the type of elementary particle which Yukawa had predicted theoretically but a considerable number of other particles as well. Indeed, Powell and other workers found so many new types of meson in the course of their experiments that they could not even keep up with their nomenclature. This created an extraordinary situation in science: for years any sub-atomic particle had to be described in great detail, listing all its properties, in order to avoid misunderstandings.

If we survey the meson types known today we can arrange them in an order similar to that in which Mendeleyev arranged the chemical elements, i.e., we can compile a periodic table of elementary particles. Some of them have positive charges, some are without charges and some have negative charges. Their masses, expressed in multiples of the electron mass, are 2,586, 2,335, 2,182, 1,837, 966, 270 and 207 respectively. The elementary particles with the mass of 1,837 are, strictly speaking, not mesons, but neutrons and protons, which we have already encountered. If the table is systematically expanded the antiparticles must be added, of which we have already met the antiproton and the anti-neutron. Now the system encompasses not only the anti-meson but also the positron or positive electron. There are still gaps in the periodic system of elementary particles, just as there were gaps in the first version of the periodic system of chemical elements, and we may hope some day to discover those "strange" particles whose properties are already theoretically indicated.

We must, however, not stray into considerations of detail, but concentrate on the essential problem, which consists in the understanding of the reason behind these basic units and of the fundamental laws governing them. There are two possible methods of approaching the problem. One is by attempting to study one type of elementary particle in the greatest possible detail and make deductions in regard to other particles. This is a very laborious method, for, while some properties of each particle are fairly easy to discover, other properties cannot, at our present technical level, be determined accurately, or even at all. In the other method we try to form a valid overall picture from a few reliably known facts—like solving a jigsaw puzzle. In either case the outcome is a mathematical expression or formula.

Heisenberg's "world" formula

The latest universal formula of this type, generally called "world" formula, was evolved by Professor Heisenberg, now Director of the Max Planck Institute for Physics in Munich.

A story is told which illustrates Heisenberg's extraordinary talents: On a fine morning in 1928 a number of students, among them Professor Heisenberg, were playing tennis in Leipzig. Suddenly Heisenberg broke off the game by saying that he had to go to the lecture theatre.

"Surely you are not going to listen to a lecture on a fine day like this?" objected his student partner.

"No, I have to deliver it!"

In fact, Heisenberg became a professor at the early age of twenty-six. When he got the Nobel Prize for his outstanding achievements in theoretical physics he was only thirty. His "world" formula (*Weltformel*), about which he spoke in Lindau, cannot be explained here, but its implications can be indicated. It is

$$\gamma_\nu \frac{d}{dx} \nu \psi + \ell^2 \gamma_\mu \gamma_5 \psi (\psi^+ \gamma_\mu \gamma_5 \psi) = 0$$

The derivation of this formula has little in common with the customary mathematical expressions. It is rather a formulation of ideas. Mathematical formulae with their symbols and calculation directives, such as "divide", "add", etc., are used merely because it is simpler and more comprehensible to express conclusions in letters and symbols than lengthy verbal explanations. First, the basic laws have to be determined, which should be as free as possible of unproved assumptions, but simultaneously embrace the widest possible field of application. That means that they deal with general, everyday, physically "primitive" experience. The next stage is the tentative combination, the weighing of contradictory premises. Finally, we reach the linking of individual thought elements by relationships. Nothing could be more off the mark than contemptuously calling a theorist who tackles such problems a fantasy-monger. It is precisely his fantasy, his imaginative approach, which shows him the way to a solution. There are bound to be many failures. Even when a theory is finally formulated, it is not always possible to use it. In order to test an important theoretical edifice such as Heisenberg's formula, it must be worked out in detail. The only way to determine its accuracy and its value is to check whether it agrees with experience.

Heisenberg based his theory on four fundamental assumptions: matter, force, causality, time. For a physicist the existence of *matter* means mass in relation to space and time. Then there are *forces*, mutual influences, interacting effects. What happens between matter and forces takes place according to certain rules, the laws of nature. Next we assume that every event has a *cause*. We believe in causality. It is evident that an effect cannot take place earlier than its cause, and the two cannot, even in a borderline case, take place simultaneously. No matter how great the speed with which an effect develops from a cause, even if it equals the speed of light, *time* is always required to produce an effect.

All these concepts and many other considerations had to be translated into the language of mathematics. Even then, this entire undertaking could make sense only if it included the ultimate constituents, i.e., the elementary particles of matter as well. The formula would have to take into consideration their properties and their inter-relations.

Future years will show whether Heisenberg's formula is correct. If it is, it should be possible to deduce from it, firstly, all the known properties of elementary particles. Existing knowledge is a touchstone of the formula's accuracy. This proof is not simple, it involves prolonged studies in mathematics and nuclear physics. Secondly, the formula should delineate the limits within which the existence of elementary particles is possible, e.g., which electrical charge distributions and mass of matter fit together in such a way as to form a consistent whole. The known elementary particles must fit into these theoretical limits. Furthermore, the formula should enable us to tell whether there exist other elementary particles still unknown to us. The formula should tell us, with greater accuracy, what inter-relationships exist among the elementary particles, and how a periodic system of elementary particles should be formulated.

But we expect from a world formula even more than this. It is conceivable that an apparent contradiction within the world formula is no proof of the latter's incorrectness, but that the very opposite is the case. In the many decades during which we have pursued science there may easily have been a source of error, which would show up only if the formula were apparently inapplicable.

Is our knowledge adequate for evolving a world formula, and have we enough data to test it? The next few years will provide the answer.

What we see is the past

The path leading from a pure contemplation of nature, *via* astronomical research and the knowledge of elementary particles to the world formula, lies before us. The assumption that the world is exactly as man sees it is separated by only a few centuries from the construction of this world formula, which will be the touchstone for the accuracy of all scientific observation. Instruments, such as the optical telescope, helped in the past to widen our view of the world, and it is to be hoped that radio-astronomy will prove of equal value now. Next to astronomy, it was atomic research, i.e., nuclear physics, which contributed much to our understanding, for it is not enough to see and record clusters of stars and masses of dust in cosmic space, a knowledge of elementary processes is also essential. When both lines of research are combined we achieve revolutionary glimpses such as that of anti-matter, and the question is raised whether there really exists just one inhabited world—our world.

We may be pleased with the knowledge achieved by our physicists and astronomers, but we should also remember how short a time has passed since we first learned to carry out accurate measurements in cosmic space with the help of our modern equipment. Are three or four hundred years of astronomical measurement enough to obtain a really comprehensive view of the universe? If we compare this short period with the age of the earth which we deduced in earlier chapters there seems good reason to doubt it. Why should we consider this particular time segment of some 10,000 revolutions of our earth round the sun as typical of all events in the universe?

Besides, we have to face what seems an insoluble difficulty, which has already been mentioned earlier. We see our "picture" of the universe, but we never see where the stars really are. When we look at them all we see is their past. We see where they were thousands of years ago, emitting the degree of brightness which we now observe. If we had accurate astronomical records going back for thousands of years we could probably deduce more information about the trends of cosmic development. Today we are constrained to use the most up-to-date equipment, to attempt the utmost limit of measurement, yet we must accept a wider margin of error in astronomy than in most other scientific calculations.

III

Let the waters under the heaven be gathered together
unto one place and let the dry land appear
Genesis I. 9

Nowhere in Genesis is any mention made of any change in the appearance of the earth since its creation. Just as creation is not yet finished, however, so the earth did not assume its final shape at the outset. Continents rise and fall, mountain ranges come into existence, oceans change their shape and the poles shift. These processes are imperceptible to the eye, but there are instruments which can record them.

Everybody is now familiar with the idea of the Ice Ages, but the Bible does not mention these extreme changes in climate.

Scientific investigations have supplied us with knowledge of how temperature variations shifted from place to place over millions of years. We know in which direction the wind blew in certain regions, and we can explain the great climatic changes that took place on the continents. Research groups in the Antarctic are now studying a continent on which vegetation once flourished and animals roamed.

The Bible draws a sharp line between heaven and earth. Today we know that there is no rigid frontier between the earth and outer space. Cosmic dust settles on the earth's surface, and gases are released into space from the upper layers of the earth's atmosphere. Vast energies interact between the galaxies.

CHAPTER 11

THE UNKNOWN EARTH

Unrecorded uranium deposits. Germany sank and rose again.
Towards the centre of the earth. Is the earth's core liquid?
We have the "knowledge" of bacteria. A floating drill on the
high seas.

WHEREVER we are, unless we happen to be in one of the few
unexplored regions of the earth, we can tell what there is to the
right and the left of us, what is in front and what is behind us.
We can survey our immediate surroundings directly. What lies
beyond our horizon we can learn from maps. With a surveyor's
chart we can even tell where, and how far away, the nearest
big tree is. We can identify on a map the location of streams,
meadows, woods, lanes, houses, villages, etc. Some charts even
show whether the woods are deciduous or not, whether the sides
of hills consist of bare rock walls or slopes covered with vine-
yards.

The air space above us has even fewer surprises for us than
the earth's surface. We can spot a jet aircraft at an altitude of
from 8 to 12 miles, if only by the vapour trail or the "blip" on a
radar screen. Telescopes watch day and night at observatories
for events which take place, or rather took place, in the universe
many light years away.

There is only one direction in which we have practically no
knowledge, even in regard to comparatively small distances.
This direction is downwards beneath our feet. We see the
ground on which we stand, but we know little of what lies
beneath the asphalt, the top soil or the pond.

There are, of course, special geological maps. The century-
long search for minerals has resulted in certain areas having
been charted with great accuracy. For instance, an English
map of 1743 shows the distribution of rock types round Canter-
bury. In 1761 a contour chart was printed which showed
details of the soil varieties around Jena, Ilmenau and Saalfeld
in Germany. Since 1866 a plethora of special maps on the
1 : 25,000 scale have been issued in Germany, and there are some
excellent survey maps in existence. It is, however, a mistake to

think that there are maps of this type for all parts of the country, even in a recording-mad country such as Germany, where everything has to be indexed and classified. Besides, whatever maps are available are generally obsolete, and for many areas in north Germany, e.g., Mecklenburg, and for the south German plain in Bavaria, no geological maps exist.

A critical reader might be inclined to regard the obsolescence of existing geological charts as of no great importance, and doubt whether the draining of a bog, the diversion of a river or the reclamation of a strip of coast from the sea since the date the map was printed would invalidate a geological map completely. Nevertheless, such is the case, for the geologist who prepared the original map had few facilities at his disposal. He could do little more than draw what he saw. He may have suspected what lay beneath the top layer of soil, but he had no definite knowledge. If, for instance, he saw clayey sand and observed that the location was the level floor of a valley he would conclude from auxiliary geological indications that this was the dried-out bed of a former lake or river. He could establish with a drill that the clay layer was, say, 6 feet deep, but that was all he could do, and the procedure was clearly inadequate. Formerly geologists were generally careful in regard to giving data about the depth of various strata, unless they could employ deep drilling or observe high vertical rock walls giving a precise indication of the order and thickness of the strata. Because of these shortcomings geologists and mineralogists are always on the look-out for features which give them further and better indications. They call them "open lodes", and the choice of them is rather limited; a gravel pit, a railway cutting, an un-usually deep excavation for the foundations of a building, in brief, any place on which excavations take place is of interest to the geologist. It is obvious that the extensive building projects of the past few years have brought about many new excavations as reference points and consequently possible improvements of the geological maps.

Unrecorded uranium deposits

The limitations in the use of older geological charts have been demonstrated in practice in recent years. Uranium became of economic and industrial interest overnight; it appeared to be even more useful than coal. The problem of locating uranium was not, however, as simple as it originally looked. Admittedly information was available about minerals or deposits in which uranium or uranium minerals occurred, and the possible locations could be traced on geological maps. It looked as if merely a little work in a study would suffice. However, unexpected difficulties arose, and experts had to admit that, in principle, uranium could occur anywhere. The existing maps were useless for uranium prospecting. There was nothing for it but to go out with a Geiger counter and start looking afresh for original or secondary deposits.

The recording of the existing state of the earth's crust had one useful result; we now know its composition with an accuracy of a few per cent. In order to avoid misunderstandings the earth's crust in this context means the firm ground of the earth's surface, but not the waters of the oceans.

If we took a metric ton, i.e., 2,204 lb, of an average sample of the earth's crust, as defined above, it would contain, *inter alia*, a large number of chemical elements:—

> 1,079 lb of oxygen;
> 584 lb of silicon;
> 171 lb of aluminium;
> 105 lb of iron;
> 85 lb of calcium;
> 60 lb of sodium;
> 55 lb of potassium;
> 48 lb of magnesium;
> 10 lb of titanium

It would also contain about 2·2 lb each of hydrogen, phosphorus and manganese. All the other, approximately eighty, chemical elements are represented by small quantities or mere traces: about 10 oz of zinc, 3 oz of nickel, $2\frac{1}{2}$ oz of copper and the same amount of tungsten; a bare sixth of an ounce of arsenic and uranium, but merely 1·5 grains troy of silver and 0·6 grains troy each of gold and platinum.

The vast amounts of oxygen and the mineral silicon with which this table starts may seem surprising to the layman, but these two elements form the chemical compound SiO_2, which is found nearly everywhere on earth in the form of sand, quartz or silicates. All basic and sedimentary rocks, e.g., slate, consist of up to 60 per cent SiO_2. The common sandstone has a 78 per cent content of SiO_2.

If we laymen know so little about what lies only from 4 to

6 feet beneath our feet the geologists themselves know little more about what lies much deeper below the surface. Nobody has yet managed to dig a hole more than 5 miles deep, and no miner has worked underground even at half that depth. The deepest hole drilled in Germany is between Rotenburg and Tostedt on the north-western edge of the Lüneburg Heath. The 17,106-foot-deep borehole is the first attempt in Germany to go deeper than 3 miles. In view of this paucity of information, the geologists' ability to recognise and describe the fundamental features of rock formations deserves admiration.

Germany sank and rose again

In the course of millions of years many changes have swept over Central Europe. The oldest geological event of which we are sure was the formation of mountains about 700 million years ago. The mountainous ridges ran from Scotland through Thuringia and Saxony into Central Europe. At that time primitive forms of life, such as algae and worms, were already in existence. About 200 million years later the ground settled and water accumulated in the sunken region, making it part of the sea from the north. There is some evidence that southern Germany was at first not involved, but later the waters closed over it as well. All these geological upheavals were combined with volcanic activity.

While the general map of Central Europe, which remained a sea, hardly changed for the next 100 million years, the animal world continued to develop. An important event was the appearance of vertebrates around 400 million years ago. The first vertebrates, the so-called ostracoderms, were strange-looking armour-plated fish, encased from head to tail in a shell consisting of bony plates.

Explanatory note to table on opposite page

Geological age determination by means of radioactive decay has produced so many additional data that a thorough revision of the hitherto accepted age periods has become necessary in the past decade. J. Laurence Kulp, Professor of Geochemistry of Columbia University, New York, critically examined the available values in 1961. We present his amended geological time scale. The oldest geological age of which we can describe the plant life is the Cambrian. We know of older rocks, but the relation between them and fossil remains in the Pre-Cambrian age is uncertain. The geological finds are more difficult to interpret, and the margin of error is so wide that further experimental material is required before a more definite statement can be made.

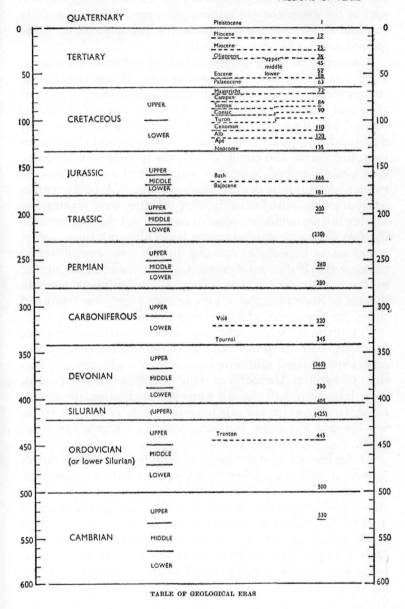

GEOLOGICAL PERIOD		AGE	TIME SCALE IN MILLIONS OF YEARS
QUATERNARY		Pleistocene	1
		Pliocene	13
TERTIARY		Miocene	25
		Oligocene	36
			45
		Eocene upper / middle / lower	52 / 58
		Palaeocene	63
CRETACEOUS	UPPER	Maastricht	72
		Campan	84
		Santon	90
		Coniac	
		Turon	
	LOWER	Cenoman	110
		Alb	120
		Apt	
		Neocome	135
JURASSIC	UPPER		
	MIDDLE	Bath	166
	LOWER	Bajocene	181
TRIASSIC	UPPER		200
	MIDDLE		
	LOWER		(230)
PERMIAN	UPPER		
	MIDDLE		260
	LOWER		280
CARBONIFEROUS	UPPER	Visé	320
	LOWER	Tournai	345
DEVONIAN	UPPER		(365)
	MIDDLE		390
	LOWER		405
SILURIAN	(UPPER)		(425)
ORDOVICIAN (or lower Silurian)	UPPER	Trenton	445
	MIDDLE		
	LOWER		500
CAMBRIAN	UPPER		530
	MIDDLE		
	LOWER		600

TABLE OF GEOLOGICAL ERAS

III

After a further 100 million years a part of southern Germany emerged from the floods. Later the northernmost parts rose as well, including the area which is now the North Sea and was part of the continent 320 million years ago. Volcanic activity continued, and submarine mountains began to form, while sedimentary rocks were deposited.

A second island emerged in Central Europe about 280 million years ago during the Carboniferous age. It was oblong and comparatively narrow, and comprised what is today the Huns-rück and Taunus plateaus and the area north of the River Main. The flora and fauna were so rich as almost to defy detailed description. In addition to tree ferns and giant horse-tails, there were also conifers. The sea teemed with molluscs, corals, snails and other animals which have long since become extinct. At this time the first saurians appeared, bulky reptiles 9 feet in length, with jaws indicating that they were vegetarians. During this period the sea receded farther, and the area between the two chains of islands became land, although there always remained a depression running in an east–west direction through the Ruhr and Central Germany, and then turning southwards towards Upper Silesia. This depression was still flooded periodically, and a lush swamp vegetation flourished there, the remains of which we now dig up as coal.

This realm of tropical vegetation did not remain undisturbed, however. The sea broke in from the north occasionally and repeatedly flooded northern Germany and considerable por-tions of southern Germany as well. When the floods receded, large lakes were left, the salt water of which gradually evapo-rated, leaving extensive salt deposits. Most of the salt seams are 170–250 feet thick, but some strata are nearly 2,000 feet thick.

At the beginning of the so-called Middle Ages of the earth's history, around 200 million years ago, the territory of Germany was largely land, but repeated flooding by the sea in the south resulted in more salt deposits, as well as the precipitation of mottled sandstone and marl, until the "marl sea", coming from the Burgundian passes, slowly flooded almost the whole country. Only a largish island remained north of where Frankfurt is today and stretching south-west from there. The rich marine fauna of that shallow sea left marl deposits up to 6,500 feet thick.

Fifty more million years passed, and the land settled and sank again, and the sea now became deeper and more extensive. Considerable changes in geological structure took place. Folds leading to fractures formed in north-western Germany, and Central German areas rose once more. There were geological upheavals in the south. One hundred and thirty million years ago the Alps emerged as folds of the earth surface. The first birds appeared, to join the early mammals of the previous era. Some of the flying creatures were winged saurians, which possibly gave rise to the later dragon legends.

Geologically speaking, our story has reached modern times, the beginnings of which are assumed to be about 60 million years ago. Geological structures now appeared which are clearly shown on today's maps. After some upheavals the Rhine valley was formed, as well as the Harz and Thuringian mountains and the Erzgebirge. Volcanic activity, occasionally with dust and lava eruptions, occurred in the Siebengebirge, the Eifel and some other places. Additional corrugations of the earth's crust raised the Alps still higher. Once more, but now for the last time, and only for a brief period, the sea swept over the swampy lowlands up to the Bight of Leipzig. It left behind, as gifts to us, lignite and amber.

This period was followed by what is generally known as the Ice Age. In our own times we come across the broken stones and rocks of this age everywhere. The original river beds, the lakes, the North Sea and the Baltic assumed their present shape.

This alternation of floods, tropical periods, droughts, heat and cold, deserts, lush vegetation and rich fauna is kaleidoscopic in its multiplicity, and applies to other and larger regions than that of Germany. In the reconstruction of this remarkably detailed picture the geologists were helped by palaeontologists, who study the ancient history of plants and animals.

All this, however, still leaves us with the question about the secrets of the terrestrial depths.

Towards the centre of the earth

In July, 1958, an oil bore hole drilled in Texas reached a depth of about $4\frac{1}{2}$ miles, a magnificent technical achievement. But if we look at it another way, and consider that the distance to the centre of the earth is nearly 4,000 miles it does not amount to very much—not one eight-hundredth of the total distance.

We have to admit that we have virtually no positive knowledge of the interior of our planet. This seems all the more astonishing if we consider the number of centuries which have passed since we learned that the earth was a globe. The earliest concept of the earth was that it was flat, i.e., a disk, but the idea that it was a globe appeared very early, though there was no proof of it. At the time of Aristotle various theories about the shape of the earth were current; it was suggested that it might be a disk, a cube, a globe or a cylinder. He compared these hypotheses and favoured the globe. He put forward not only all kinds of philosophical arguments in favour of this contention but also the observation that during a lunar eclipse the earth's shadow invariably looked round. Eratosthenes (275– 214 B.C.) based his ideas on Aristotle's and succeeded in determining the circumference of the earth by measuring the shadow cast by the sun. He deduced that the distance between Alexandria, where he lived, and Syene (now Aswan) was one-fiftieth of the earth's circumference. He over-estimated the size of the earth by only 15 per cent. We should realise that the people of the ancient world had a fairly clear picture of the shape of the earth, in fact a much truer picture than existed in Europe around 1500, when the earth was still visualised as a disk which supported the vault of the star-studded sky.

From the time when man first began to drive shafts into the earth he marvelled at the strange subterranean world. He spun legends and fairy-tales about the ore, the metal and the precious stones to be found there, and endowed them with guardians in the shape of pixies, spirits and gnomes, who flitted through the mine shafts and corridors in the flickering light of candles and torches. Our knowledge of the earth's interior was, however, not greatly increased by these tales. One of the earliest factual observations was that it was always warm in a mine, and that the deeper one went the warmer it became. Later measurements showed that the temperature increased by 1° C (1·8° F) about every 80 feet. This fact immediately suggested the calculation of the temperature 5, or even 50, miles below the surface, and led to the conclusion that the centre of the earth was immensely hot. It was decided that the core of the earth, at a temperature of the order of 190,000° C must be in a molten, incandescent liquid state. Even the more realistic estimates of today range from 1,000° to 12,000° C, a very wide margin typical of man's ignorance of the earth's core. An article published in 1960 postulated, on the basis of recent measurements, a temperature of 2,900° C. Fundamentally, however, we have

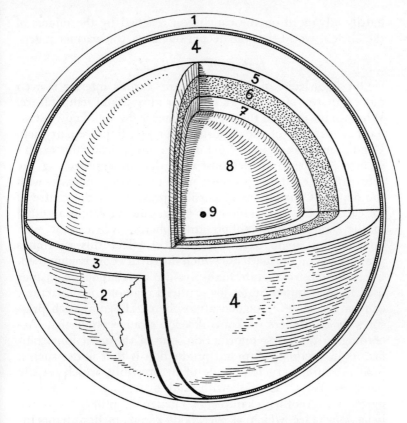

Model of "shells" of the earth, based largely on assumptions, because we still have no certain knowledge of the inner structure of our planet. The only points which all hypotheses have in common is that in the interior of the earth there are various zones with different properties, and that the iron content increases towards the centre of the earth. The zones are probably not sharply defined, but merge into each other

1. Atmosphere (312 miles). 2–4. Rock mantle: density 3·4, volume 123,000 million cubic miles, weight $1,714 \cdot 10^{15}$ tons. (2. Fracture zone: density 2·6. 3. Fluid zone: density 3·0. 4. Primeval mountain shell of very heavy rock: density 3·4, depth 75–750 miles; outer edge: isostatic surface, pressure about 28,000 atmospheres, temperature about 1,450° F; inner edge: pressure about 500,000 atmospheres, temperature about 2,900° F.) 5–7. Intermediate layers (Depth for 5—over 1,000 miles; 6—up to 1,500 miles; 7—over 1,800 miles): Density 6·4; volume 98,500 million cubic miles; weight $2,581 \cdot 10^{15}$ tons; either silicate with metallic admixtures, or sulphides and oxides, of which 70 per cent are iron sulphide; nature of subdivisions unknown. 8. Iron core: density 9·6, volume 42,900 million cubic miles, weight $1,685 \cdot 10^{15}$ tons; 88 per cent iron, 6–10 per cent nickel, remainder predominantly carbon, phosphorus, cobalt and platinum, rigidity several times that of steel. 9. Centre of the earth (depth 3,880 miles); pressure about 1·5–3 million atmospheres; temperature presumably 3,000–4,000°C.

hardly advanced on the conclusion reached by the miners of the ancient world that the deeper one goes, the warmer it gets.

Is the earth's core liquid?

Our knowledge of pressures in the earth's interior is even more a matter of guesswork than our ideas about temperature. What we measure on the earth's surface is the well-known standard air pressure of one atmosphere or 14·7 lb per square inch. Conditions change as we get farther away from the earth's surface. It has been demonstrated that in approaching the centre of the earth the pressure in the rock strata increases with the depth. Calculations of possible pressures at the centre of the earth on the basis of these sub-surface measurements resulted in the figure of 3·5 million atmospheres. We cannot even imagine, let alone test, what sort of effect this enormous pressure has on the matter of which the earth's core is composed. Even the most elaborate high-pressure installations, e.g., that used in the United States for artificial diamond manufacture, can barely achieve 100,000 atmospheres. Even at such pressures the substances we know develop strange properties. According to the latest information, one of the most important factors in synthetic-diamond production is that under such a high pressure a crucible made of pyrophyllite, which usually melts at 1,315° C, can withstand a temperature of over 2,630° C. Another example of change in properties is the behaviour of ice, which, as everybody knows, melts at temperatures above 0° C. Subjected to a pressure of 45,000 atmospheres, it remains ice even when heated to 220° C. Hot ice seems a contradiction, but its existence can be demonstrated.

Even if the pressure in the interior of the earth is considerably less than the above-mentioned 3·5 million atmospheres, we can still expect a few surprises in exploring the depths. This lack of knowledge is one of the reasons why there are numerous theories about the earth's interior below the accessible surface layer. Volcanic eruptions early led to the assumption that the earth was solid, but riddled with hollow spaces, crevices and rifts containing hot liquid lava. In one of his fantastic stories Jules Verne described travellers who reached the earth's centre through a former crater opening.

Another assumption about the core is that it is liquid, or even gaseous. The observation of volcanic activity for a long time led to erroneous conclusions. It seemed logical to draw conclusions about the conditions in the earth's interior from volcanic eruptions. The geologists of former ages regarded a volcanic crater as a kind of window into the earth's core.

Volcanology is a fairly old science. Pliny the Elder's enthusiasm for knowledge cost him his life during the eruption of Vesuvius in A.D. 79. He bravely advanced into the area of hot ash and hot stones in order to discover the cause of this natural phenomenon, and was asphyxiated by hot gases.

For a long time descriptions of volcanic eruptions were as far as science went. Chemical and physical knowledge was inadequate to create a picture of what went on in the interior during an eruption. Nobody knew where the magma originated, how it got to the surface, what caused the heat emission, where the water came from which caused volcanic steam, how craters originated, and how and when eruptions took place. It is only recently that a start has been made in answering these questions scientifically.

Magma cannot possibly come from an incandescent liquid earth core. It lies originally at a depth of 30 or 40 miles, and becomes as liquid as we observe it only when it reaches the edge of the earth's crust.

It rises slowly from its original depth and collects in secondary accumulations from 1 to 4 miles deep, from where it is finally expelled during an eruption. Even today scientists have no clear idea of the origin of the enormous energy required for the heating of the magma. Some think that there are heat currents in the earth's crust, others that some energy-emitting chemical transformations, perhaps oxidation or other reactions, take place in volcanic gases. Others, again, wonder whether in certain areas local overheating is caused by the friction of the shifting of vast rock areas. The assumption that the heat is derived from radiation chemical transformations is extremely unlikely, because volcanoes would then emit radioactive substances, and that has never been observed.

It is possible to conclude that vast amounts of water have been emitted by volcanoes, including hot water and gas geysers, in the course of the various geological ages. At a depth of 20 or 30 miles magma can contain up to 10 per cent water.

Many volcanic events and activities have been scientifically investigated in the past few years, but this has not yet led to any substantial increase in our knowledge of the earth's interior.

Any scientific theory about the earth's interior must be able to explain two things: its density and its "shell" structure. We know from various calculations the approximate weight of the earth. Expressed in tons, the figure starts with a 6 and has 21 noughts after it. The important property in this case is the so-called density, i.e., the weight ratio to an identical volume of water. The figure is 5·5. While the whole of the earth is thus about 5·5 times as heavy as if it consisted of nothing but water, this ratio does not apply to the earth's crust, the average density of which is barely 2·7 or 2·8. Something in the core must be so heavy as to bring the total average up to 5·5. But what is it?

The second problem is this. Earthquakes or nuclear explosions cause tremors to travel through the earth. Sensitive instruments can record these with great accuracy, as regards both intensity and time. Unless the tremor originates exactly where the instrument is located, the latter records the same tremor more than once. The explanation is simple: A seismic wave, i.e., the shock wave of the earth tremor, travels along the earth's surface until it reaches the recording instrument. A similar wave also travels through the interior of the earth until it reaches the instrument. Sometimes interior shock waves are reflected by the earth's crust, and then the record shows the same tremor four, or sometimes even five times within a quarter of an hour. If, as is usually the case, it is known where the tremor started the paths of the shock waves can be calculated. Analysis of these phenomena leads to the conclusion that the earth consists of concentric shells of matter of different densities.

Before we explore the nature of these shells we shall list them in their order. All geologists are agreed that the earth has a core and a crust. The thickness of the latter is estimated at from 25 to 60 miles. Between the crust and the core there are two other layers, going down to about 600–1,800 miles. There is hardly any doubt that the substance of the earth's crust is granite and basalt of various kinds. As regards the substance of the next layer there are at least six different hypotheses. Some assume a liquid magma shell, some a substance similar to the composition of a stone-and-iron meteorite, some class it simply as "silicates". The suppositions about the matter constituting the earth's core are not less varied. The majority view favours a mixture of iron and nickel, but there is no certainty whatsoever about whether the core is solid, liquid or, possibly, gaseous.

It seems disgraceful that, while living on this earth, improving our technical achievements from day to day, and now, standing on the threshold of conquering interplanetary space, we have neglected to study seriously the earth beneath our feet. Not to put too fine a point on it, we know as little about what we live on as bacteria know of the medium on which they grow.

A floating drill on the high seas

The simplest way of acquiring knowledge about the earth's crust would seem to be a systematic deep drilling programme. Such a project would, however, be as expensive as space flights, and a large-scale systematic research programme is therefore out of the question as long as the earth's crust remains uninteresting from the military point of view, and military interest in it is the last thing we desire. If drilling became feasible, however, the best place for it would have to be determined. There is no sense in starting on top of a mountain. The deeper down a drill hole is started, the cheaper it is. If it were possible to drill at sea, perhaps in a submarine canyon 6 miles deep, a great deal of effort would be saved. The idea is sound but, knowing the huge contemporary drilling towers and how firmly they have to be mounted, deep drilling from a ship at sea appears hardly feasible.

No ship can be anchored at sea firmly enough for a rotary drill many miles long to be operated without bending or breaking. Turbo-drilling methods, which have been very extensively developed in the Soviet Union, seem more promising, for the hollow drill shaft remains at rest, and only the electrical or hydraulic turbo-drill at the end rotates.

There is another reason for favouring drilling at sea. According to an earlier theory, the continents "float" like thick rafts or ice floes on a comparatively viscous layer. In that case there would be little point in drilling through the depth of the continental floe. The oceans are almost free of these continental floes and their fragments, although, of course, there are various sedimentation layers on the bottom of the ocean, but their thickness is, comparatively speaking, small.

The most attractive aspect of drilling in the depths of the ocean is the prospect of reaching the so-called Mohorovičič

Discontinuity, and possibly piercing it. This layer is named after Dr. Andrija Mohorovičič, Director of the Meteorological Observatory in Zagreb, who in 1909 studied the seismographic curve of a relatively small earthquake the centre of which was about 25 miles south of Zagreb. Mohorovičič's instrument accurately recorded all the tremors. There was the wave that travelled along the earth's surface, there were waves which went down into the interior of the earth, were reflected and then recorded. But there were also jagged points in the recorded curve which could be explained only if the waves travelled along a deep layer in the core at a greater speed than in the outer crust. The wave velocity along the rock crust is about $4\frac{1}{2}$ miles per second, but along the Mohorovičič Discontinuity it is over 5 miles per second.

There may be several possible explanations of this phenomenon, but which is its true cause? It seems that the Mohorovičič layer is the outer shell of the earth's mantle, the outline of the original shape of our planet.

Both in the Pacific and in the Atlantic oceans there are areas where the Mohorovičič Discontinuity is only about 8 miles below the bottom.

Is there a chance of reaching this original earth's surface within the next few years? Even the smallest traces of fine drilled dust from a single successful drilling at that depth would cause a scientific sensation.

An experiment of this type was launched in the United States and called the Mohole project. The first drillings were made in March, 1961, by a special ship off the California coast at an underwater depth of about 3,100 feet. As the vessel carrying the drilling rig could not be anchored, she was held in position within a range of 33 feet by four outboard motors. At a third attempt a depth of 310 feet was achieved, which, in view of the target, was very poor.

A similar experiment was attempted near the island of Guadalupe off the California coast, at a spot where the underwater depth was over 12,000 feet. At first there were no difficulties. The diamond drill bit cut easily through the thick sedimentation layers at the bottom. At 570 feet, however, the work was held up, for the relatively soft sedimentation layers had come to an end and the drill had reached hard igneous basalt covered by a thin layer, three or four hundredths of an inch thick, of volcanic glass. This indicated that the rock had at some time been in a molten state. As far as could be ascertained, the lowest sedimentary layer was not bonded with the glass, which meant that the sediments settled on the basalt after it had cooled rather than that hot, liquid basalt had pushed up into a much thicker sedimentary layer. The level of the sedimentary layers had thus actually been reached. Drilling was continued for another 44 feet or so with considerable difficulty. A high temperature was recorded at the bottom of the drill hole, twice as high as the average for oceans.

The results of these efforts do not look very encouraging; 614 feet is not very deep. However, for the time being this was not so important. The fact that a hole was drilled at all more than 2 miles under water, and that drilling was carried on for some considerable time, should be regarded as a success.

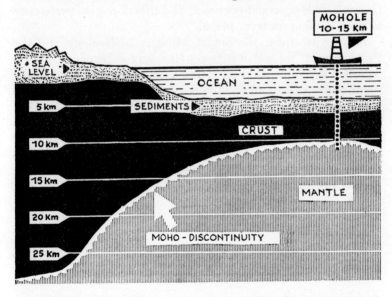

Diagram of a Mohole drilling. On the left the outline of a continental shelf. It should be possible to reach the Mohorovičič Discontinuity through the sediments and the earth's crust at the bottom of the ocean. Based on DEA Archive

It is to be hoped that future drillings will yield more information about the unexplored interior of our planet. Even now we can deduce from the Mohole drillings that rich vegetation and animal life were prevalent about 25 million years ago at what is now the bottom of the Pacific Ocean off the Mexican coast. The favourable conditions for vegetation and animal life around the Guadalupe area continued for about 7 million years and then began to deteriorate. Today few organisms are to be found there.

The reaching of the Mohorovičič Discontinuity seems now to be a question of time and money. The drilling near Guadalupe was generously financed by four oil companies, who put $3 million into it. The drilling vessel was called *Cuss*, from the first letters of the firms' names: Continental, Union, Shell, and Superior. They were looking for oil and found none, but they achieved something else: they increased our knowledge of our planet.

The Soviet Union shows considerable interest in American plans and achievements, but apparently not purely for scientific reasons. The Soviet authorities like combining fundamental research with practical purposes, and therefore give preference to deep drilling on terra firma.

In August, 1962, the Soviet Ministry of Geology and the Protection of Natural Resources (the very existence of such a Ministry is significant) considered whether five drillings to the depth of from 6 to 8 miles, should be made in the low-lying areas near the Caspian Sea. This would give Soviet scientists the opportunity for studying the conditions governing oil and gas deposits at a great depth, a scientific problem of considerable importance in regard to the origin of oil. The technical difficulties of this kind of drilling, however, are not less than of the deep-sea drilling experiments.

CHAPTER 12

TRAVELLING CONTINENTS

Battleships and clay particles. Ancient winds. Wegener's theory of continental drift. India was once at the South Pole.

FEW subjects arouse as much general interest as international rivalries in the field of science. The launching of a rocket is not really a sensation unless someone else is doing the same thing. Competition makes for suspense. Whose rocket will fly higher? Whose satellite will stay up longest, or produce the most interesting results? Whose expedition will first reach the summit of an unconquered Himalayan peak? Which nation will send the first manned rocket to the moon?

About the turn of the century everybody was fascinated by the race to the Poles. In 1895 Nansen's famous expedition failed to reach the North Pole. In 1908 it was reached by the American Peary, who had made an unsuccessful attempt in 1906. In December, 1911, Amundsen planted his flag on the South Pole, where it was found by his British rival Scott when he reached the spot in a state of exhaustion. His diary expressed his disappointment at not being the first man to reach this objective. Discouraged and weakened, he started on his return trip in a snowstorm, and died of exhaustion, the last survivor of his party.

What is the driving power that forces explorers to seek the North Pole among the vast ice floes, or the South Pole over the 13,000 feet high, glacier-covered plateau of the Antarctic? Perhaps the Poles are physically and geographically the most interesting points on earth. There are no longitudes, or, if you like, all longitudes. There is no east or west. Every direction from the North Pole is South, every direction from the South Pole leads North. Time, too, stands still, for no star rises or sets, and the sun's path is a circle parallel to the horizon. The Poles have even more peculiar features: they wander, and so does the axis of the earth with them. The fluctuation is not very great, but every 435 days the Poles travel in a randomly varying orbit around the true position within a range of up to

11 feet. Is this the reason for the divergence between the geographical and the magnetic Poles? The magnetic North Pole is near 70° latitude North on the western side of the Canadian peninsula Boothia Felix. If we draw an imaginary straight line from the magnetic North Pole to the magnetic South Pole in Victoria Land it does not pass through the centre of the earth.

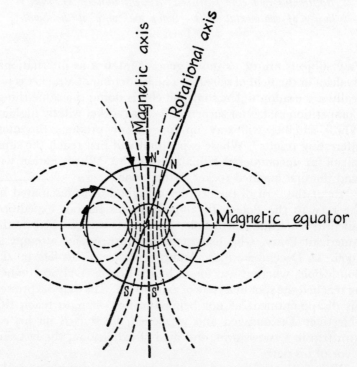

The magnetic lines of force of the geomagnetic field. The magnetic axis of the earth does not coincide with its rotational axis

In response to the earth's magnetic field the so-called "south pole" of a compass needle points to the magnetic North Pole. If you look at the compass while you are at that point the compass will show no definite direction. It has become useless. If we tilt the compass so that its vertical axis is horizontal the needle which had pointed north now points downwards. Similar but reversed phenomena may be observed at the South Pole. Halfway between the two Poles lies the magnetic equator. If we tilt the magnetic needle into a vertical plane there it will remain horizontal, provided it is not affected by local magnetic fields. One could imagine that the lines of force enter the earth at the magnetic North Pole, come out again at the magnetic South Pole, and then, like the lines of longitude, run back to the north.

All this is knowledge which one picks up at school, but recent years have produced staggeringly new ideas.

Battleships and clay particles

During the last war a group of scientists in Germany was concerned with the problem of how to demagnetise a battleship. It was an important problem, for magnetic mines, i.e., naval mines which responded to magnetic attraction, had become a lethal weapon. To start with, we must understand why ships are magnetic.

The building of a modern ship starts with the laying of a keel. This large "iron needle" lies in the earth's magnetic field. While steel sheet, ribs, etc., are riveted in position, the entire iron structure is shaken by millions of vibrations, and the hitherto magnetically disordered elementary iron particles, the so-called magnetic areas, have the opportunity of shaking down into an orientated position in relation to the earth's magnetic field. The finished vessel is one huge magnet, and becomes an excellent target for magnetic mines. Now, what can be induced can be destroyed again, preferably by changing the position of the ship in relation to the magnetic field, while it is still in the yard.

An ordinary ship at sea, in calm air and resting completely motionless on the water, would turn like a compass needle in the north-south direction. If it sank it would, in an ideal case, still lie in the direction of the earth's magnetic field even under water. It is clear that such a ship, when found centuries later, would still show where the North Pole and South Pole were at the time of its sinking.

Large accumulations of iron, such as modern ships, do not, of course, occur in nature. Finds of metallic iron of terrestrial origin are very rare, but we know of several minerals which have magnetic properties. There are fine iron oxide grains scattered in various types of clay. Experiments have shown that, if we take a lump of such clay and mix it with sufficient water to make it liquid and then let it settle again, the iron oxide particles form a pattern orientated along the earth's magnetic field. Every particle acts like a small magnet. They settle not only in the direction of a horizontally balanced magnetic needle but also more or less vertically downwards, in accordance with the geomagnetic field. Of course, the precipitation of these particles can be affected by currents in the water. Besides, the clay sludge which is precipitated simultaneously slightly smudges the clarity of the pattern, but basically the particles obey the same laws as a magnetic ship.

The earth is full of ancient clay deposits. In Sweden and elsewhere the clay sediments of Ice Age lakes were examined for their magnetic orientation. They undoubtedly show what the earth's magnetic field was like thousands of years ago.

We know of other similar sedimentation minerals, such as slate and sandstone. Some sandstone deposits have indubitably retained without change the magnetic orientation of their iron oxide content for 150 million years.

Ancient winds

A surprisingly large number of new facts about the history of the earth are becoming known. Do we know which way the wind, if any, blew in geologically ancient days? If we examine the large sandstone areas near Laramie, Wyoming, we find that the sand which formed the stone was not shifted and deposited by the sea, but was blown into dunes by the wind. There is nothing unusual about that, and similar sandstone areas can be found in many parts of the world. The sand always contained very fine magnetic mineral particles. The wind stirred up this mixture, and then nearly all of it settled down again, orientated according to the geomagnetic field. Measurements showed that the predominant wind in Laramie was a north-east wind. Similar investigations resulted in ancient wind charts of extensive regions, and palaeological wind maps of the world will probably be produced in due course.

Wherever magnetically responsive particles are given the opportunity to settle in an orderly manner, they do so, e.g., those in still liquid lava streams. We can demonstrate it by melting a piece of lava and letting it cool and solidify again, as has been done in many laboratory experiments.

The conclusions drawn from these observations appeared correct until lava deposits were found in Iceland, Japan and Central France which were magnetically the reverse of what had been expected. Where they should have had the magnetic north, they had south, and vice versa. A very tempting theory

IDAHO

WYOMING

o
Rock Springs

o Laramie

o Salt Lake
City

Great
Salt Lake

Denver
o

UTAH

COLORADO

o Alamos

ARIZONA

NEW MEXICO

o Phoenix

Roswell o

Chart of ancient winds in the Colorado Plateau, showing the directions in which winds blew sand 300 million years ago, as shown by today's sandstone

was put forward, namely that the magnetic field of the earth had been reversed many million years ago.

Fortunately it was possible to find, at least in a few cases, a faultless, complete, but complicated answer. These cases were phenomena of secondary self-magnetisation. The lava in question contains two magnetic minerals, and at higher temperatures one of them becomes magnetically oriented, while the second is still in the melting stage. Magnetic forces are therefore already active in the lava, when, on cooling, the second constituent becomes solidified. The magnetic forces in the melt are now in a direction exactly opposite to the geomagnetic field. Therefore the second mineral settles in a magnetically reverse direction. When the lava is finally quite cold the magnetism of the first mineral may be so small compared with that of the second that it is virtually negligible. Our magnetic measurement, which deals with the total magnetisation of the sample, therefore shows a displacement of 180°. In spite of this explanation, the entire situation is by no means yet clear. As far as we know, there are some reverse-magnetised lava deposits to which the above-mentioned principle of reverse magnetisation cannot apply. Lava investigations have revealed another interesting effect. Hot liquid lava which flowed over magnetically orientated basic rock had wiped out the latter's magnetisation by its great heat. As soon as the lava cooled, the basic rock again became magnetic, but this time under the influence of the lava's own magnetic field. Examples of this have been found in Iceland, France and Arizona.

Wegener's theory of continental drift

William Gilbert, physician to Queen Elizabeth I of England, is regarded in scientific history as the founder of the theory of electricity and magnetism. In 1600, three years before his death, he published his most important work, *De Magnete*. In the third chapter of Vol. IV we find a rather surprising reference to the magnetic forces of the earth:

> "If there is no general dissolution of a continent, or the sinking of one as described by Plato and the Ancients, in the area where Atlantis had been, the magnetic direction will remain constant."

No doubt the concluding phrase is correct, but we do not know what happens when the map itself changes.

Many geologists and physicists feel ill at ease in regard to the idea that continents are not firm, fixed and immovable. They hesitate to subscribe to the theory of continental drift because they do not see clearly why the land masses of the earth should move. They admit that on the map it looks as if the western coast of Africa fits into the eastern coast of South America. Is the Atlantic Ocean really just a stretch of water which flooded into a gap in a once undivided land mass which later separated? Wegener's continental drift theory answers this question in the affirmative.

A polished fragment of the iron meteorite which fell in Sikhote Alin in Siberia in 1947. It weighed 4 lb 9 oz. The black, outer layer is clearly visible. The inside has been ground flat to make the coarse-grained structure visible

Widmanstätten etched patterns on the Toluca meteorite. The inner fine structure found in iron meteorites is called after A. v. Widmanstätten, Director of the Fabrik-Produkten-Cabinett in Vienna, who discovered this phenomenon in 1808, but did not publish his discovery until 1820

The famous Arizona meteorite crater viewed in the north-west direction from an altitude of over 3,000 feet. The similarity with moon craters in regard to light and shadow effect is striking. The photograph was taken on July 12th, 1958 at 7 a.m. by John S. Shelton, an American geologist, when the rising sun lit the crater from a low angle

Johannes Kepler, painted in 1620. Seven years later the great astronomer asked the Strassburg library which owned the picture not to exhibit it publicly, as it was not a good likeness. However, no better portrait of him has ever come to light

Symbolic picture of man breaking through the vault of heaven in order to learn about new celestial spheres. Woodcut from about 1530

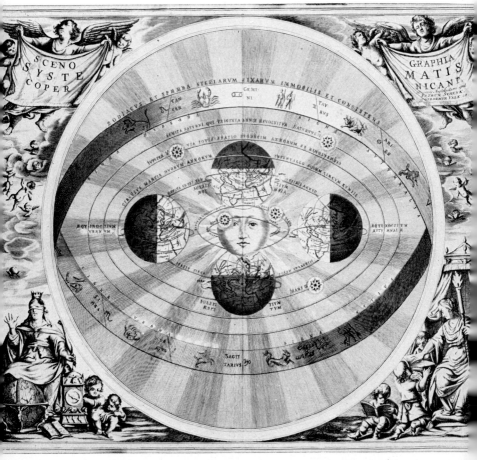

Picture of Copernicus's world system in the stellar atlas of Christoph Cellarius
(Keller), a Grammar School teacher who was one of the first in Germany who
dared to explain the new world picture in a school

The nearest galaxy to our own Milky Way is the Andromeda spiral nebula. The light takes about 1,500,000 years to reach the earth, i.e., we see this formation in the location where it was 1,500,000 years ago, and in the shape it had at that time. Without a telescope this galaxy can be seen only as a tiny speck of light

Spiral nebula in the constellation of Canis, as seen through the 60-inch telescope of the Mount Wilson Observatory

Night photograph of the largest German radiotelescope on Mount Stockert in the Eifel. The 87-foot aluminium parabolic dish (depth 18 feet) can be turned and tilted

The Fraserburgh, Nova Scotia, radiotelescope, built by the Stanford Research Institute of California in 1951 for the study of aurorae and similar phenomena. Its 108-foot parabolic mirror proved capable of sending radar signals to the moon, and these revealed data on the structure of the moon's surface

Photograph of the tracks of anti-matter in a bubble chamber filled with liquid propane in which the passage of particles leaves a temporary trail of propane vapour bubbles. An anti-proton coming from above collides at (1), where the track breaks off, with an (invisible) proton, and splits up into a neutron and an anti-neutron. The latter collides with an atomic nucleus at (2) and destroys it. There are five traces of decay particles

Dominique François Arago (1786–1853), physicist and astronomer. Together with Gay-Lussac, he published the famous *Annales de physique et de chemie*. He popularised the scientific research of his time and was one of the first authors of the factual type of natural science books

Dmitry Ivanovich Mendeleyev, Professor at St. Petersburg University, born 1834 in Tobolsk, Siberia, died 1907. He evolved the periodic system of elements and explained it in a textbook written for his students in 1868

Professor Werner Heisenberg lecturing at a Nobel Prize winner Conference, Lindau, about his "World formula"

Landing vessel of the Soviet South Pole expedition on the coast. Even during the Antarctic summer there is very little vegetable and animal life. During the winter the rocky landscape of the coast is covered with ice

Inside the comfortable and well-equipped radio station of the Soviet Antarctic Station at Mirny, which serves not only as a communications centre but also for recording electro-magnetic phenomena in the atmosphere

Launching a weather balloon in the Antarctic. The motions of the rising balloon indicate wind velocities and wind direction at great altitudes, etc. This type of balloon can also be fitted with radio transmitters to obviate the need for optical observation

Members of the British expedition on their way from their ship to the Antarctic coast. Large drifting icefloes frequently prevented the direct unloading of ships at the coast. In spite of using ice-breakers the U.S. expedition, too, had to make several attempts before they could land on the Antarctic continent

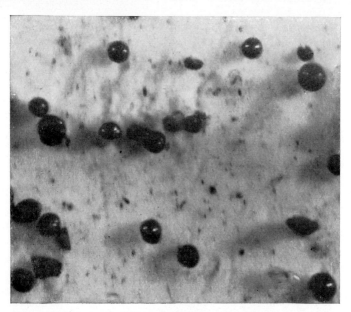

Cosmic pellets in the Western Pacific, magnification 200. This
sample from the ocean bed was taken by the Swedish deep sea
expedition in 1947–48 on the M.S. *Albatros*

Sediment core, longitudinal cross-
section. Sample taken south-west
of Cyprus at a depth of about
8,300 feet. There are numerous
fine strata. The white layers are
mostly chalky ooze, the darker
layers are mixtures of organic
substances or volcanic material

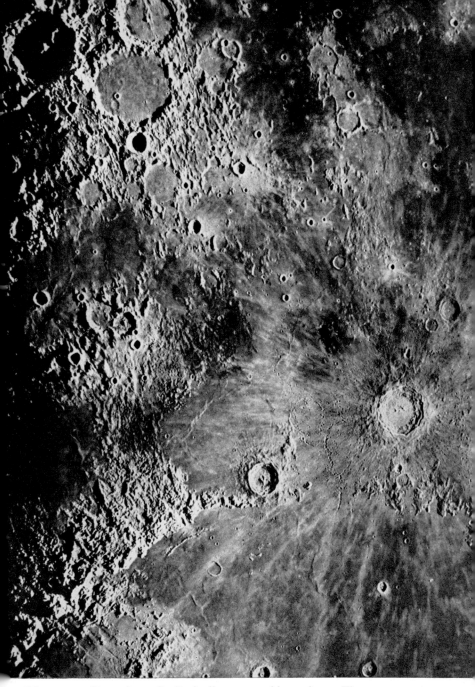

Moon crater Copernicus, 56 miles in diameter, and its environs. There are extensive level plains with lightly undulating ground, and also some rugged mountains. Strangely enough, the whitish surface lines do not lead to the centre of the crater on the right. The slight hollows on the left at the foot of the crater are also unexplained. The smaller craters in the plain must have been created later, as the time sequence is obvious from the surface structure. The origin of some distinct linear formations is also a mystery

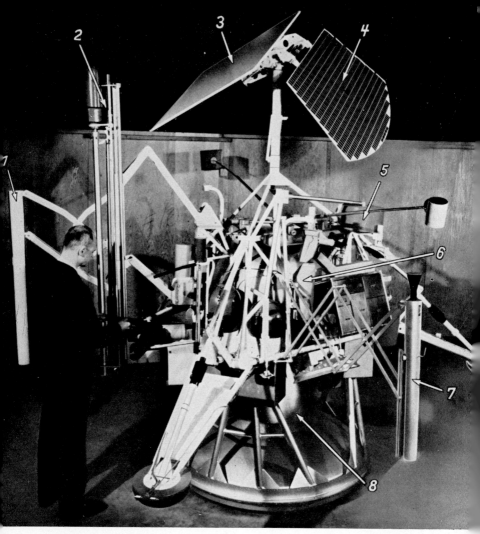

Model of a moon laboratory to be landed automatically on the moon, designed for the National Aeronautical and Space Administration of the United States. Before landing, the station will, with four television cameras, take and transmit photographs of the moon. Retro-rockets will ensure a soft landing, after which a moon drill will take soil samples down to 20–60 inches deep for immediate analysis by the built-in instruments. The probe will transmit for a month information on gravity, radioactivity, composition of any available atmosphere, etc. Weight of the instrument head: 770 lb, height about 12 feet. 1. Neutron counter. 2. Drill. 3. Antenna. 4. Solar batteries. 5. Geophysical instruments. 6. Television camera. 7. Geophysical probe. 8. Nozzle of retro-rocket

Friedrich Wöhler (1800–82), professor of Chemistry at Göttingen University

The first sample of urea synthesised by Friedrich Wöhler is kept in the Deutsches Museum, Munich, in a test-tube marked with Wöhler's name. The test-tube at the bottom of the picture contains a sample of aluminium isolated by Wöhler. The test-tube is hermetically sealed so that the aluminium should not lose its shiny surface by oxidation in air

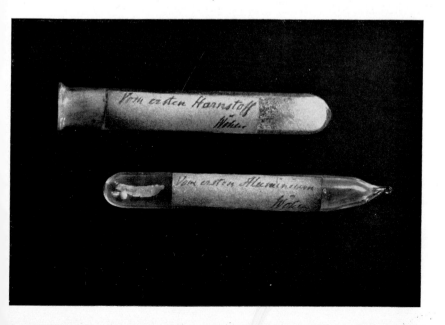

Harold C. Urey, 1934 Nobel Prize Winner for Chemistry, has contributed to fundamental research on isotopes, investigated the moon's surface and given decisive impetus to research on the origin of life on earth

Stanley Miller, Urey' assistant in the Chicag University Laboratory experimenting on th synthesis of amino acid under simulated primeva conditions

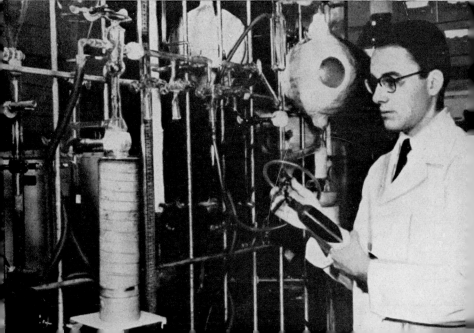

Alfred Wegener, a talented German geophysicist who perished in the ice of Greenland in 1930, first propounded his theory in 1912. He started out from observations of the similarity in the development of plant and animal life, and in early climatic developments on both sides of the Atlantic. He maintained that South America had drifted westwards from Africa, and that the separate land masses of the southern hemisphere had once been one land mass round the South Pole. He maintained that the continents were simply floes of lighter material, floating and drifting on a heavy, viscous, deeper layer.

This theory caused a sensation. Most geologists rejected it as too far-fetched, as geologically impossible, and as an idle speculation. It was the "scientific hangers-on", as it were, who tried to verify the theory, and found that numerous facts became comprehensible in the light of Wegener's ideas. Though he left much unexplained, and the picture had to be expanded or amended in some details, his theory still represents a considerable advance. If it is a fact that continents drift, the magnetic constituents of their minerals should be oriented in a way which corresponds to the earth's magnetic field at the time of their formation. Wherever magnetic minerals are discovered to deviate from, or lie athwart, the magnetic field, a possible rotation of the land masses in question has to be at least considered. Wherever the angle of the magnetic field lines does not correspond to the present latitude, a drift towards, or away from, the magnetic pole must be suspected.

Measurements showed that the continents had, indeed, shifted in relation to the magnetic pole.

The clay deposits in Britain show no measurable anomaly in the past 15,000 years, but sandstone samples irrefutably indicate a drift of Britain towards the north in the past 150 millon years. It has travelled northwards from about the 17th degree of northern latitude, i.e., from about the level of French West Africa. The estimate shows a present rate of drift towards the north of 10 feet per century. But that is not all. During that time Britain also turned clockwise about 37°.

India was once at the South Pole

If Britain were the only land mass for which such a proof could be produced there could still be doubt about whether the land masses or the magnetic poles had changed their location. When the corresponding measurements on the North American continent were compared with the British measurements a certain similarity was found to exist. However, the conditions in Australia are totally different. Australia drifted around the South Pole for a long period. At least fourteen different locations could be verified, some right next to the Pole, others

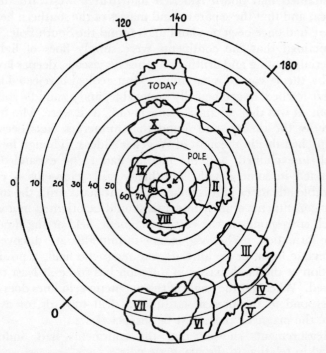

The meandering of Australia in relation to the South Pole. The figures indicate the succession of positions. Some intermediate stages have been left out for the sake of clarity. The earliest location is next to the present position of the continent, on 180° longitude and between 10°–40° latitude south. Then Australia moved past the Pole to the equator, and then again towards the South Pole. There the continent turned round and drifted to its present position

farther away but in alignment with the Pole. The area where Sydney is today had sometimes been pointing towards the South Pole and sometimes away from it. As far as we know, the Melbourne area must have been near the Pole for a considerable period. At that time Australia took a half-turn round the Pole, and the Melbourne area was near the pivoting point. Parts of South Africa and South America too were near the Pole and were blanketed by glaciers. At some time in the past 300 million years South Africa must have drifted right across the South Pole. India too moved about considerably. Magnetic investigations of Indian rocks show that as recently as 70 million years ago India was south of the equator. Two hundred million years ago it was right next to the South Pole. Greenland drifted about in warmer regions; sometimes it approached the equator in the area of the present-day Pacific Ocean. Finally, there is a strong possibility that the distance between the American and European continents is actually still increasing.

We have been able to determine the land distribution on earth for 500 and more million years. These investigations explained many hitherto incomprehensible geological observations. In the course of the British expedition's crossing of the Antarctic in 1958 coal was found near the South Pole. This contained remains of plants similar to those found in South African coal. This showed that the Antarctic land mass had at some time enjoyed a warmer climate. We know of areas in Australia, South Africa and India which indicate that the land was once completely icebound, and we know why there are in Germany and Britain vast areas of sandstone formed from dry, wind-blown sand.

There is another possible, even probable, explanation. Not only did continents drift and oceans change their shape, not only did the position of the magnetic poles shift, but even the axis of rotation of the earth may have altered. This possibility will be tested in the years ahead. If the large land masses of the continents drift, the big spinning-top called earth can hardly be expected to remain unaffected. There is also a reverse relationship, i.e., if the position of the rotational axis of the earth shifts, the forces affecting the continents change, and the latter may start moving. It is obvious that the distribution of land and water is not random, there are certain fundamental regularities. There is hardly a land mass on the globe that is balanced by another on the opposite side. Almost at any spot on terra firma a vertical line through the centre of the earth would end in water on the other side.

If we summarise the results of magnetic measurements made up to now they present a consistent picture. For instance, it is possible to draw on a globe all the points at which the North Pole has been located, as seen from, say, India. A curve drawn through these points would start in the northern part of South America, run across Florida, Mexico, the United States and

Canada, to the point where the magnetic North Pole is today. Magnetic measurements of the oldest rocks indicate the apparent position of the North Pole in South America, where our curve starts. In the course of later geological periods the indicated direction towards the North Pole has shifted, as mentioned above, to reach its present location.

A similar curve of the apparent location of the North Pole in the course of geological ages can also be drawn up from the viewpoint of North America. In this case the curve starts in the Pacific Ocean and passes south of Japan into China, crosses Siberia and ends again at today's magnetic North Pole. Similar curves can be drawn for Europe and Australia.

When all these curves are examined together it begins to look improbable that the cause of these strange travels of the Pole could be other than the drift of continents. If the magnetic field of the earth had reversed, as some people maintain, or if the position of the magnetic poles had shifted, the curves would be similar. As, however, the bends in the curves traced by the wanderings of the Pole vary, the probable answer is the drift of continents.

We do not yet know to what extent the continents, seen as a whole, have moved in relation to each other. Perhaps it will soon be possible to recognise a general line of drift and draw conclusions about the forces causing all the related phenomena. The idea that processes in the earth's interior are responsible for all these events cannot be dismissed. The earth has found no lasting stability yet, and nobody knows whether it will ever assume a final stable shape.

We cannot yet formulate a definitive conclusion about the meaning of the geomagnetic investigations for the determination of the continental drift. Research in this field is still too young. It is certain, however, that geomagnetic methods have proved very valuable. The agreement of the outcome of this work with conclusions arrived at by other means justifies our hopes of this method. A report of the Conference on Continental Drift at Atlantic City in 1960 stated: "It [i.e., the idea of continental drift] has advanced from being a doubtful hypothesis to a credible theory."

CHAPTER 13

A BELEMNITE'S DIARY

Cuttlefish remains serve as a thermometer. How cold was the
Ice Age? Interrogation of Australian molluscs.

WHAT was the temperature of the ocean in the autumn of
160,000,000 B.C.? The question sounds preposterous, but the
answer is available: 66° F. In the winter of that year it went
down to 64° F, but next year there was a remarkably hot summer and the temperature of the water went up to 70° F. The
two subsequent summers were slightly cooler, but the water
temperature, even in winter, did not drop below 62° F. However, we do not wish to exaggerate our chronological accuracy,
and are prepared to admit that those lovely warm winters may
have occurred a million years earlier or later. We shall not
argue about the exact location of the stretch of water in question
either, but the accuracy of the quoted temperature variations
is beyond doubt.

The French physicist and mathematician Arago, mentioned
earlier, would have given much to have known these facts. In
1833 he engaged in strenuous efforts to discover data about
changes in the climate of Europe. Extracts from the tables he
compiled are quoted below:

866 The Adriatic Sea and the River Rhône were frozen
     solid. (A complete freeze up of the Rhône near
     Arles and some other places in Provence in 1776
     implied a temperature of at least −18° C (0° F),
     according to observations made at that time. When
     the Gulf of Venice froze in 1709 the thermometer in
     Venice dropped to −20° C (−4° F).)

1133 The River Po was covered with ice from Cremona to
     the estuary. The Rhône could be crossed on ice.
     Wine froze in the wine cellars (i.e., at least 0° F).

1234 The Po and the Rhône were frozen. Supply carts
     crossed the frozen Adriatic (−4° F) to and from
     Venice.

1468 In Flanders soldiers had their wine supplies divided

133

into rations by axes, according to Philippe de Comines.

1638 The water of Marseilles harbour around the galleys was covered with ice floes ($-4°$ F), according to Papon, IV, 490.

1716 The Thames was frozen. Stalls were erected on the ice in London.

Arago quotes Strabo, the Greek geographer, as the authority for disagreeably cold temperatures in ancient times:

"Strabo relates (*Geographica*, Book II) that frosts were so severe at the mouth of the Palus Maeotis that one of Mithridates's generals threw back the cavalry onslaught of the barbarians on the very spot where they had been defeated in a naval battle in the previous summer."

Arago came to the conclusion that changes in the average temperature, if any, were very slight over the centuries.

Cuttlefish remains serve as a thermometer

For a long time it was accepted as an axiom that the proportion of all isotopes, the pure forms of chemical elements, always remained the same in a substance. The carbon clock showed that this assumption was wrong. The carbon-14 content, however, decreases merely because ^{14}C decays in the course of time. One would have thought, therefore, that if all isotopes were stable, the mixture ratio of isotopes in a substance would be constant anywhere on earth. This, too, is a fallacy.

If we put a kettle of water on a hot stove it eventually begins to boil. As everybody knows, water is a compound of two elements: hydrogen and oxygen. Oxygen has two isotopes of different weights: oxygen-16 and oxygen-18. All water particles containing oxygen-18 are, therefore, relatively heavier than those containing oxygen-16. When water boils, water particles evaporate into the air as steam, and it is easy to see that the heavier particles, being less volatile, tend to remain in the kettle. Scientifically speaking, the oxygen isotope ratio in the remaining water has shifted in the direction of the heavier isotope.

We know now that such changes in the isotope ratio occur in many cases, particularly when a new solid substance is formed from an aqueous solution. For instance, when a layer of chalk is formed, the ^{16}O — ^{18}O ratio differs, depending on whether the temperature of the chalk is 30° F or 77° F. A relative change of 0·096 per thousand in the oxygen-18 content can be observed for a degree (F) change in temperature.

How do we know how warm or cold it was on earth 160 million years ago? The answer was provided by a belemnite, a kind of cuttlefish, or rather by its fossilised remains, popularly described as a "thunderbolt". A belemnite started life in autumn and like a snail, built a shell for itself. As it grew, its shell grew too. The ratio of oxygen-16 and oxygen-18 in the walls of its shell changed with the temperature of the surrounding water. In the spring of the fourth year of its life it died. Some years ago its fossilised remains were examined layer by layer, and the oxygen-18 content was determined, and consequently the temperature of the water in which it had spent its life was established. It is possible that the belemnite deceived us. Perhaps it lived in lower and warmer layers of water in winter, and perhaps it migrated to cooler seas in the summer. We shall never know. But we can read the "diary" it kept about the temperatures it experienced 160 million years ago. It is a pity that it died so young; its "thunderbolt", the shell covering of the lower part of its abdomen, was only just over an inch thick.

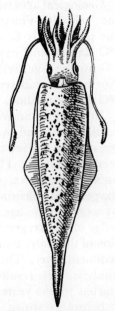

Reconstruction of the appearance of a belemnite, a kind of cuttle-fish of the Jurassic and Cretaceous Ages. The pointed lower part is frequently found as a fossil, and popularly called "thunderbolt" or "Devil's finger". Belemnites up to 7 feet long have been found

How cold was the Ice Age?

The above-mentioned method of determining temperatures of ages long past has been developed fairly recently. It is likely to expand considerably in the near future. Then we shall be able to have tables of prehistoric temperatures. The method can be applied not only to fossilised remains of animals and plants but also to crystal or mineral formations. Salt deposits at springs can show us the temperature of the spring water in earlier ages, and salt mines the changes in temperature of the evaporating ocean from which they originated. Finally, the fossils of former ages, such as molluscs and crustaceans, can be examined and compared with present-day varieties of a similar kind whose climatic preferences are known.

Geological ages which are not too remote should be examined more closely. For instance, in regard to the Ice Age we are in the particularly favourable position of being able to combine ^{14}C dating and oxygen-18 temperature determination. The Würm Ice Age, referred to as the Wisconsin Ice Age for the North American regions, falls largely within the range of the ^{14}C dating method.

In order to answer the question about the temperature on earth 10,000 and more years ago, research on sediments in the oceans was carried out. Drill cores from the bottom of the sea were examined. They contained calcareous shells of marine animals, molluscs, etc. Chalk is a combination of carbon, oxygen and calcium. The carbon-14 content enabled workers to ascertain the age of a particular drill-core layer, and knowledge of the oxygen isotopes ratio made possible the determination of the water temperature at the time of the formation of the sediment layer. The calcium did not unduly interfere with the analysis. The results were unequivocal: a period of severe cold started 70,000 years ago. Thirty thousand to 40,000 years ago it became warmer, but it was still colder than today. About 15,000 years ago a generally warmer period ensued. These discoveries formed a promising start for this method. On the other hand, investigations revealed strange events which we still do not understand, such as the fact that 11,000 years ago there was a warming up of the Atlantic, but apparently not of the Pacific. Did ocean currents alter their course, perhaps? It is known from carbon-14 measurements of peat, molluscs and wood that in the past 10,000 years the level of the seas rose in proportion to the extent to which polar ice caps melted.

Interrogation of Australian molluscs

Correct determination of the geographical location of the test samples is of vital importance for future research into past sea temperatures.

The most recent of the geological ages is called the Quaternary, and its earliest subdivision is the Pleistocene (Diluvium), a rather extensive period from about 550,000 to 20,000 years before our time. During it Heidelberg man, *homo heidelbergensis*, appeared and heralded the beginning of the Stone Age. Northern Germany was repeatedly buried under thick glacial layers. There were periods of severe rain. The glaciers in the Alps reached fantastic lengths, and the Black Forest, the Bohemian and the Carpathian Mountains became icebound. Not only Europe was caught in a cold grip but also New Zealand and the Andes in South America, for instance.

At that time the coast of California was inhabited by a profusion of molluscs of various types, but they were not cold-water mollusc types. Analysis of their shells showed a temperature of about 52° F, with a margin of error of $\pm$ 1 per cent. Investigation also revealed which molluscs preferred shallow, warm inlets and which types lived in deeper and cooler water regions. Such a detailed analysis of the past led to the question of today's temperatures in the same geographical location. This comparison took into account the fact that a mussel does not grow at the same rate throughout the year; it builds its shell more slowly in winter than in summer. A study of present-day temperatures between February and August in the same area showed variations between 50° F and 58° F as compared with an isotope-determined past temperature of 52° F. This agreement of figures is astonishing, but we should beware of concluding that the climate of California has not changed over thousands of years. Temporary variations of temperature are certainly conceivable, and in any case, the climate of a region is not determined by temperature alone. We do not know whether there were gales, or rain, or thunderstorms.

Investigations of mollusc shells in South Victoria, Australia, take us even farther back into the history of the earth. Geologists set the beginning of the Tertiary geological age at around 60 million years ago, and, as this age covers a long time period, it is subdivided, the latest period being the Pliocene. The earlier periods are the Miocene, the Oligocene and the Eocene. The Australian mussel shells which were examined by the $^{18}O/^{16}O$ method belong to the three latter periods.

What was happening in Europe at that time? It was a period of repeated floods and the growth of huge forests, the remains of which are still mined as brown coal (lignite). The crust of the earth was in motion; mountain ranges piled up, fractures, dislocations and volcanic outbreaks were not infrequent. An extensive range of mammals developed gradually, after the dying out of the fantastic giant reptiles of the earlier Jurassic and Carboniferous ages. In brief, the climate of the region which later became Europe was very favourable, and occasionally resembled the Mediterranean climate of today.

In Australia conditions at that time were not much different. In Victoria, too, there are brown coal deposits and traces of volcanic activity.

The investigations of mussel shells confirm the previously known facts:

Upper Miocene	61° F
Lower Miocene	70° F
Oligocene	68° F
Eocene	57° F

The average temperatures of 64–66° F, estimated for those periods for Europe, are thus probably correct in view of the similar geological conditions as established for Australia.

The correct measurement of ancient temperatures is still very difficult. Although the obtaining of samples is a simple matter, the measuring equipment and methods are very complicated. Highly sensitive mass spectrometers are required, and skilled staff to use them. The results have to be interpreted with great care. The ratio of oxygen-16 and oxygen-18 content cannot yet be accepted as an absolute criterion of the water temperature of former ages. The possible dependence of the measurement results on the effects of the locality has to be judged, as well as the possible subsequent changes of the calcareous shells of animals in the course of geological ages. In many cases the temperature estimates have been found to be unreliable, and it will take much more experience before the method can be regarded as a routine standard research process.

Luckily, a control method has been found recently, when it was discovered that the ratio of the carbon isotopes $^{12}C/^{13}C$ also depended on temperature. This opened up the possibility of applying a usable, even if not an exact and unequivocal, method for verifying ancient temperatures. This method can be of practical importance for obtaining otherwise inaccessible data in cases where there is no risk of any considerable changes in the material under investigation. This became known at the Congress on Isotope Separation Methods, held in Paris in the summer of 1962, where it was announced that a temperature dependence, similar to that of oxygen-18, existed for the deuterium content of water and ice. Scientists are now able to establish the temperature which obtained in the cloud from which the rain originated This is of particular interest when the precipitate is not rain but hail, i.e., ice. Oddly enough, our knowledge of the origin of hail and snow-crystal formation is very inadequate, in spite of the attention given to this problem in recent years for military reasons, because of the desirability of avoiding the formation of condensation trails by high-altitude aircraft.

A hailstone, weighing just over one-tenth of an ounce, was melted layer by layer, and no fewer than 384 temperature determination tests were carried out on this sample in exploring the temperature zones of its formation.

By the same method we can determine, from the deuterium content of the ice of glaciers, local and seasonal temperature variations over the past 1,000 years.

CHAPTER 14

THE EARTH BURIED UNDER WATER
AND ICE

*Metals from the sea. The calendar of sediments. Nuggets
from space. The new pole of cold. Research in the Antarctic
night. How thick is the Antarctic ice?*

DURING the Second World War the American ship *Cape
Johnson* was sailing in the Pacific. Her skipper was H. H. Hess,
in civilian life a geologist at Princeton University, who could not
forget his special subject even in the middle of a war. One day
the ship's echo-sounding device recorded strange phenomena:
underwater mountains of a hitherto unknown shape—steep
mountains with flat tops, plateaux up to 25 miles in diameter,
like stunted volcanic cones without peaks. No such mountain
shapes had ever been recorded in geological literature, and their
origin was a puzzle.

For millennia oceans had covered about 150 million square
miles, or 71 per cent of the total surface of the earth. For all the
knowledge that had been acquired of the continents, little was
known in 1940 about the underwater part of the earth's surface.
Reefs and sandbanks near the coasts had been charted, and
navigation maps showed the depths of the sea more or less
accurately, but that was all.

Round the continents there are submarine shelf areas where
the ocean bed slopes downwards gradually and the depth of the
sea rises to 200–600 feet. These shelf regions indubitably belong
to the adjoining land masses. They have a kind of natural landscape, with hills, valleys, drift blocks, etc. These areas have
certainly been dry from time to time, perhaps when large masses
of water in the form of ice covered the continents, and the level
of the oceans was lower. Maps showing the earth if all continents rose by 660 feet, i.e., showing the shelf areas as dry land,
have for a long time been part of all geographical work. However, it would be erroneous to suppose that a further corresponding increase in dry land would show if the continents were
raised slightly more. At the outer edge of the continental shelf

areas the bed of the ocean suddenly drops 2–3½ miles without an intermediate gradient.

What does the ocean bed look like? The eroding effects of rain, wind and frost are absent. Apart from a few mountain ranges, one imagines the bottom of the sea to be flat. Even if it had not been flat originally, the organic and inorganic remains of fish, molluscs, cosmic dust, etc., dropping down on to it for

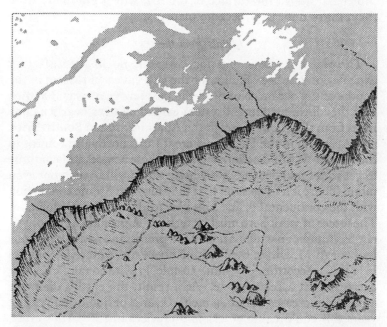

The Canadian and U.S. coastline of the Northern Atlantic. What we know as solid land is only a greater elevation of the continental land mass which continues under water up to the steep drop where the relatively level shelf area ends. The mouth of the Hudson continues along the shelf

millions of years would surely have levelled out any abysses and crevices. We know today that this picture is totally wrong. The ocean bed is formed by volcanic eruptions, submarine springs, strong currents, and plant and animal life. Its landscape is just as varied as the landscape we see on dry land.

The steep, sloping edge of the shelf area, the place where the ocean really starts, is of particular interest. No mountain range on dry land is comparable in height or steepness. In places there have been extensive submarine landslides, and elsewhere the shelf has clefts and winding valleys which look like canyons

141

and may be the beds and estuaries of former rivers. Science has not yet found a definite explanation of these features, but it is noteworthy that near the Congo, the Ganges, the Hudson and other rivers there are such canyons in the continental shelf.

The formation of the mountains discovered by Professor Hess during his wartime voyage is easier to explain. These "guyots" or table mountains are remnants of volcanoes that originally protruded above the surface of the sea, which gradually wore them away until they became plateaux.

Metals from the sea

Theories have been put forward, but no final satisfactory explanation has been found, for the vast caved-in ravines in the depths of the ocean. Not until the past few years was it known that they form a coherent system extending over nearly 44,000 miles from the Arctic through the Atlantic, around South Africa and Australia to the Pacific, where it turns north and returns to the Arctic. We do not know whether these abysses still continue to get wider and deeper, and whether they will branch out even more. There is a suggestion that they may have some connection with the continental drift. This idea leads to much speculation. The forces at work here must be terrific. A prominent geophysicist has sought an explanation of the process in an idea expressed by Paul A. M. Dirac, the British Nobel Prize winner for physics in 1937. According to him, cosmic gravitational forces are decreasing at a certain rate. As a result, the earth's diameter annually increases about $\frac{1}{50}$ inch. Over a period of millions of years this could cause cracks and crevices in the earth's crust, and result in earthquakes, marine quakes and, perhaps, even the continental drift itself. Observations up to now have been too few to give us a definite picture of this process.

A sailor is interested in the surface currents which affect his ship; to a biologist the sea means a profusion of creatures and plants of many varieties; for a meteorologist and climate investigator the oceans are huge heat exchangers; but for a chemist they are treasure-houses of minerals. One cubic mile of sea-water contains about 160 million tons of salts. About 78 per cent are ordinary cooking salt and of little value, but about 10 per cent are magnesium chloride, and a further 5 per cent magnesium sulphate. If there were some way of isolating them on a large scale at reasonable cost it would be of great economic and technical importance. Attempts to solve this problem have

been made, but so far only the bromine content of sea-water has been utilised. About 90 per cent of the known reserves of this element are contained in the oceans.

Of all the attempts to make the sea yield up its mineral treasures, Fritz Haber's plan for obtaining gold from sea-water caused the greatest sensation. When Germany had to pay its war debts after the First World War he calculated that the extraction of gold from sea-water would be a paying proposition. Unfortunately, the analysis figures which he quoted in support of his plan were wrong, and the then known methods of gold extraction inadequate. Today the situation may not be quite so hopeless. It seems feasible that suitable ion exchangers could be developed which would selectively enrich gold, uranium or other heavy metals. A cubic mile of sea-water could yield roughly £8 million or $22 million worth of gold, provided the price of gold remained stable.

The boldest plan for the extraction of the sea's treasures, however, does not concern the water but the bottom of the sea, not in the more easily accessible shelf areas, but in the ocean depths. The distribution of deep-sea sediments has been known roughly since 1891, when the report of the British *Challenger* expedition was published. Until then it had been accepted as a rule that the diatomic (algae) sediments, calcareous shells or red deep-

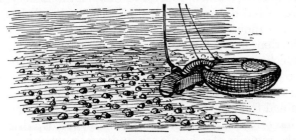

Proposal for a "giant vacuum cleaner" for the collection of manganese nuggets from the ocean bed

sea marl were deposited evenly and then lay undisturbed on the ocean bed. Today we know that this assumption was false. In the depths of the oceans there are currents which strip the sea-bed bare in places. Arctic water flows at a rate of nearly a mile an hour southwards near the bottom of the sea. Wherever this current passes, the sea-bed is swept clean, and sediments are found only in the lee of considerable rises. Colour photographs show this clearly. They also show the unexpected sight of vast areas of sea bottom covered with manganese pellets. Near the Society Islands in the South Sea these ore nuggets are the size of a fist and contain 25 per cent manganese, 15 per cent iron, and a little copper, nickel and cobalt. If it is true that about 10 per cent of the ocean bed is covered with this ore the oceans contain the richest manganese deposits on earth. These findings have been confirmed by Soviet researches. American firms, including the Vanadium Corporation of America, have started drawing up plans for the exploitation of these deposits. Huge vacuum cleaners have been suggested for collecting these ore fragments from the bottom of the sea. The plan is quite feasible.

The calendar of sediments

Even where currents are absent, sedimentation does not proceed evenly. By means of highly elaborate drilling, or rather pile-driving procedures, samples 65–100 feet long can be excoriated from the sea-bed. In many ocean areas these samples consist of calcareous remains of foraminifera (*Globigerina*), tiny creatures about $\frac{4}{100}$ to $\frac{8}{100}$ inch long. A closer examination of these sea-bed samples shows very fine stratification which originated from summer and winter sedimentation respectively. Therefore one can read off the years just as in the case of rings of a tree-trunk, though the reading here is much more difficult, as every inch of sediment represents about a thousand years. In the case of red deep-sea marl, the thickness is still less, about $\frac{1}{3}$ inch in a thousand years.

Deductions about the contemporary water temperatures can be made from the type of foraminifera in the various layers, because it is known which types predominated at certain temperatures. For instance, the effect of the latest Ice Age can be determined from the succession of types. The calendar of sediments has other entries, too. Occasionally there is a discoloured layer, the remains of volcanic ash, indicating extensive volcanic eruptions. The hope, however, of calculating the total age of

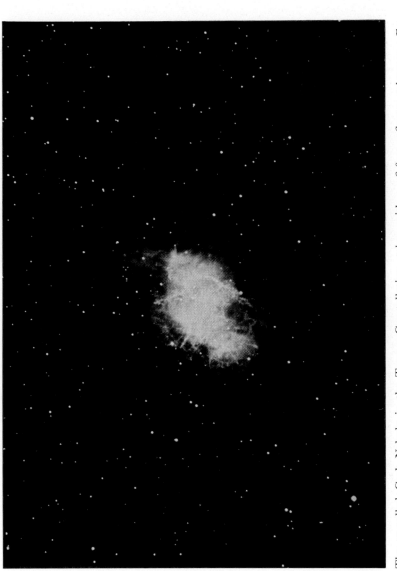

The so-called Crab Nebula in the Taurus Constellation, taken with a 16-foot reflector telescope. Exposure time 4 hours and 45 minutes

The Orion Nebula. Colour photograph by the Mount Palomar Observatory
reflector telescope

oceans is still illusory. The older sedimentation layers are mostly very thin, less than ¼ inch for a thousand years, as far as can be determined from samples obtained so far. It is still impossible to obtain drill cores which go down to bedrock in the ocean. If we assume an age of 2,000 million years for the Pacific the sedimentation layers should be about 2 miles thick according to estimates, but we do not know how thick they really are. Echo-sounding tests yielded the strangely low figure of 100 feet. Is the Pacific really ten times younger, only 200 million years old? Or are the lower sedimentation layers so compressed that they reflect sound exactly as if they were bedrock? The Mohole research may give the answers.

Nuggets from space

Regularly deposited deep-sea sediments make possible the study of a problem which is of even greater interest in regard to the history of the earth.

In 1874 Eric Nordenskiöld, the well-known Swedish geologist and natural scientist, read a paper to the Stockholm Royal Academy of Sciences, which greeted it with incredulous astonishment. He had examined snow which had fallen near Stockholm and found in the samples a blackish, magnetic powder. Later he melted snow samples from the Arctic which yielded similar results. Chemically speaking, the powder consisted of iron with a little cobalt and nickel. What was puzzling was how this powder had got into the snow. Nordenskiöld announced without hesitation that it was cosmic dust. He went further, and asserted that, if this black metallic powder was being precipitated all over the earth there should be half a million, perhaps even a million, tons of it coming down in a year.

Two years later, in 1876, Sir John Murray found "cosmic pellets" in deep-sea sediments. From 2 pints of red deep-sea marl he extracted, with the help of a magnet, twenty or thirty pellets, each less than $\frac{1}{100}$ inch in diameter.

In 1946 the *Albatros* expedition obtained large drill cores from the deep sea, going through 50 feet of sedimentation layers. These cores were like a picture-book of eras lying 15 million years back. They too contained these "cosmic pellets" with varying densities of distribution. Sometimes there were fewer than fifty pellets per lb of sediment, sometimes there were thousands. Usually there were more in the later, higher layers. Chemical analysis of the pellets confirmed Nordenskiöld's analysis of nickel, iron and cobalt and, additionally, there was copper. This confirms the origin of the powder found in the snow as meteorite iron. Apparently considerable quantities of meteoric matter descend continuously to the earth in the form of a fine rain of metallic powder.

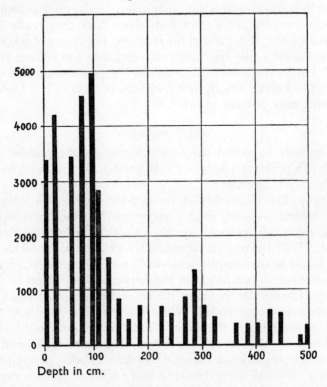

A 17-foot-long drill core from the Western Pacific contained the above number of cosmic pellets per 1 kg (2·2 lb) sediment. The number of manganese pellets decreases with depth. This observation was confirmed by other samples

The quantities of this cosmic dust can be measured by analysing air. One cubic mile of air contains about 2 oz of nickel. By extending this calculation to the entire cosmic dust content we arrive at a figure of about 26 lb per square mile of air, or 5 million tons annual precipitate over the whole earth. By working "backwards" we realise that 5 million tons a year over the whole of the surface of the earth mean merely $\frac{1}{30}$ oz per square foot in 1,000 years. These figures coincide more or less with the results of the analysis of deep-sea samples.

We may be sure that in the future deep-sea sediments will contribute much information on the history of the oceans and therefore add to the picture of the development of the world. Even today we could ask whether the dust in the atmosphere has other effects besides making a measurable contribution to sedimentation, i.e., an increase in the mass of the earth. This effect is on rather a small scale. Besides, we could only become aware of it when the quantity of dust sedimentation changes, e.g., when the earth is subjected to meteorite showers. E. G. Bowen claims to have discovered a possible connection. According to some observations, a meteorite shower is followed four weeks later by a period of increased rain. Bowen assumes that cosmic dust increases the number of condensation nuclei for water vapour normally present and so accounts for the rain. Should this supposition be generally true, meteorite showers and cosmic dust would prove to be important factors affecting the climate of the earth.

There can be no doubt that the oceans still harbour a multitude of surprises. An expedition of scientists from Columbia University, New York, headed by Maurice Ewing, discovered vast salt deposits, so called salt domes, at the bottom of the Gulf of Mexico. Apparently these deposits date from the Jurassic age, when the region was covered by water to a depth of many thousands of feet. Similar salt domes are known on the American continent along the coastal plains, and on the continental shelf of the Gulf of Mexico.

Other strange phenomena are the vertical currents in the Pacific along the California coast. Such rising or descending currents may be much more frequent than has hitherto been supposed. They occur in the Atlantic and the Indian Ocean too. These currents were discovered by means of under-water television and film cameras. They result in an interchange of water at various depths, and have been shown to arise from large wave movements occurring at a certain depth under the surface, in places where cold layers meet the warmer surface layers.

Investigations showed that a large area in the Pacific, starting south-east of Hawaii and stretching as far as the American continent, is a "biological desert" where there are virtually no living organisms. It had been known for some time that there was little plant or animal life in these regions, but there was no explanation of why organisms were so rare there. An attempt

to catch living creatures at very great depths, during which
66 million gallons of water passed through the nets, yielded a
quart bottle of marine organisms, mostly minute insects.

The main reason for the unfavourable conditions for life in
this sea area is the total absence of those vertical currents which
carry food from the bottom of the sea to higher levels.

The new pole of cold

On August 9th, 1958, the Soviet observation station Sovietskaya in the Antarctic reported a ground temperature of
−81·7° C (−117° F). This station is one of forty-six scientific
stations established for the exploration of the Antarctic within
the framework of the International Geophysical Year. Its
location is favourable—about halfway between the geomagnetic South Pole and the so-called Pole of Inaccessibility.

The temperature of −117° F is the lowest ever measured on
the earth's surface. The Soviet scientists had beaten their own
cold record, as it were, by 68° F, for until then the lowest
recorded temperature was that measured in north Siberia in
February, 1933. Today we regard the Sovietskaya station situated at 78° 24′ latitude south and 87° 35′ longitude east,
12,100 feet above sea-level, as the Pole of Cold. This temperature is, however, more than a local record. Measurements in
the Antarctic show that the South Pole area is in general the
coldest region on earth. One of the reasons is that there is land,
"icy cold" land, under the ice at the South Pole, while the
huge ice cap of the North Pole floats on the sea, the temperature
of which is about 32° F. No matter how thick the ice layers
may be, they are still inadequate insulation against this "heat
reservoir".

Research in the Antarctic night

Until 1958 very little was known about Antarctica. If we
look at an atlas printed in the 'thirties it shows little more than
the fact that an Antarctic continent exists. Its outlines were
more or less known at that time, and on its edge there were a
few names here and there. This, however, applied only to
coastal strips which were known, or were believed to be known.
Even the outline of the coast was indicated only tentatively in
places by slightly curved lines between two points at which
land had once been seen. The other wide spaces of the Antarctic were blank spaces on the map. They were left white, not to

show that they were covered with ice and snow, but because they were unexplored, and no cartographer knew of any features that could be entered on a map.

In 1957 a little had been heard of some mountains, and the outlines of the Antarctic continent became a little more accurate. At some places a good guess could be made of where the land ended under the ice fringe, which stretched right into the sea, in other words, where the actual coastline was situated. The bulk of the continent, however, was still an unexplored blank area.

Geophysicists chafed under the awareness that large parts of the earth's surface with their water and air cover were virtually unknown. There were only suppositions, some reports by expeditions and a few aerial photographs. A few pictures of rugged ice mountains and storm-swept rock walls, however, and the knowledge of a few mountain ranges were not enough. What sort of land lay under the ice?

In 1957 the problem of the Antarctic was tackled on a large scale, as regards both men and money. Some of the men had previous knowledge of the region, which is as large as Europe and the United States combined. One of these was Captain Finn Ronne, a Norwegian by birth, the commander of the American base Ellsworth, who had been in this locality with a small party during the previous year, and in 1957 was preparing to winter in the Antarctic for the fourth time. His report of his preparations is impressive. It covers the voyage in ice-breakers and transport ships and the difficulties in constructing a station on the inhospitable plateau of the ice shelf. Hundreds of tons of material had to be unloaded in record time, because if the timetable were not kept there was danger of the transport ships becoming icebound. This would have led to tremendous difficulties, if not to catastrophe, as, instead of a handful of men, hundreds would have had to live on the same stores of food. Prefabricated buildings had to be erected and equipped for the long polar night. Observation towers and radar installations were erected, for the team wanted not merely to survive, but to do scientific work involving thousands of measurements. Sensitive recording instruments had to be maintained in operational condition so that they could work uninterruptedly. In addition to the geophysical tasks, there was also biological work to be done. Even apparently simple things are important to the specialist, for neither ice nor snow samples are all alike. Ice samples had to be systematically collected from various depths; these had to be packed, recorded and preserved for later, more accurate examination at home.

Everything had been thoughtfully provided: good living-quarters, a more than adequate supply of food (later it transpired that, in spite of the modern oil-heating installation, the consumption of food was enormous), automatic washing machines, handicrafts supplies, records and a library, a special sledge, heated vehicles for exploration trips, in short, the thousand-and-one things required by a party of people who would be isolated for months in an icy waste. Still the enterprise remained an adventure, in spite of all the technical help provided, as a small party found to their cost when they flew to a point in this infinite loneliness to take a few measurements. It was intended to collect them again quite soon, but a fierce snowstorm suddenly broke, as it often does there, and it was not until a fortnight later that they were brought back to safety. On another occasion a special vehicle almost fell into one of the huge snow-covered ice crevices almost 300 feet deep. Some time later help had to be given to a British expedition which was attempting to cross the Antarctic with its tracked vehicles. An extensive, rough ice plain which they traversed had exhausted their fuel supply, and they had to wait until an aircraft with petrol supplies reached them.

How thick is the Antarctic ice?

When we look at a sketch-map of the Antarctic we observe first a large bean-shaped land mass, glacier covered, partly bordering on the sea and partly encircled by several mountain ranges. It is still impossible to say definitely how much land there is under the ice, i.e., land above sea-level. Soviet explorers have recorded the profile of the ice on a trip to the Pole of Inaccessibility. Their record shows that in the foregound of a high mountain range of over 6,500 feet, islands and peninsulas, as it were, exist; i.e., in places the ice goes down below sea-level.

Beyond this mountain range there is a very broken stretch of country. Its bays are largely filled with glaciers, to an extent which leads to the supposition that solid South Polar land lies below the ice. Sometimes the ice masses covering the surface of the sea engulf some of the islands. The above-mentioned bean-shaped part of the land surrounded by water and mountains is over 6,000, and in places even over 13,000 feet above sea-level. The hills on the other side of the mountain ranges reach 6,500 feet in but a few places. One mountain range ends in a narrow peninsula and continues in a semicircle of ever-decreasing islands. This chain of islands, resembling the Antilles, can be followed farther to Cape Horn in South America.

The explorers' first surprise came from the ice itself. They

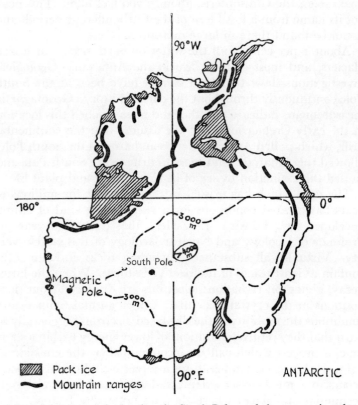

Map of the Antarctic showing the South Pole, and the magnetic pole, as well as pack ice and mountain ranges

had estimated its thickness in hundreds of feet, but their estimates proved to be much too small. The team at the American Byrd Station, situated about 5,000 feet above sea-level, measured the ice below them and found it to be 8,600 feet thick. If the ice should ever melt in this locality the ocean floor would be 3,600 feet below, and there would be no dry land.

Not far from the American station lies a mountain range—

part of which is called the Sentinel Mountains. Here there are five peaks of over 13,000 feet, and one of them is nearly 15,600 feet high. This range is, geologically speaking, very young, with high rock walls, sharp ridges and wide glaciers along its flanks. The Horlick Mountains, discovered in 1934, belong to this range. The 6,500–9,500-foot-high peaks have almost vertical north walls. American scientists have climbed some of these peaks, e.g., the Glossopteris, about 9,700 feet high. This peak got its name from a fossil fern of the Carboniferous period, and it can be found there in large quantities.

About 1 per cent of all the water on earth occurs in frozen glaciers, and most of these are in the Antarctic. Geological investigations show that land cannot have been at the South Pole continuously throughout the earth's history. Geomagnetic measurements indicate that the land mass reached this location in the early Cretaceous Age. We assume that the continental drift, which pulled Australia across and around the South Pole, allowed the Antarctic land mass to drift to the South Pole and caused the extinction by ice of its rich animal and plant life.

The cold which has existed in the Antarctic for millions of years has created conditions for a very special kind of dating developed by Edward J. Zeller, the thirty-four-year-old Professor of Geology and Nuclear Geology of Kansas University. Virtually all substances, including rocks and minerals, contain at least traces of radioactive isotopes. When the latter decay, giving off radiations, electrons are displaced from their positions in the crystal structure. Under normal temperature conditions the mobility of the displaced electrons is generally so great that they return to positions of lower energy within a short time, a process which can be accompanied by the emission of light. If, however, temperatures are relatively low this process occurs to a much lesser extent, and more and more electrons accumulate in places where they do not really belong. If a mineral in which many electrons have been thus stacked in the wrong places for millennia is heated it is possible to observe a peculiar luminescent effect. The intensity of the light given out by the sample is proportional to the original content of radioactive substances in the material, and to the period of time during which "frozen" electrons have accumulated. This light effect, called thermoluminescence, is nothing new. It had been observed long ago, but it is Zeller's merit to have carried out systematic investigations in the Antarctic by its means. This is a far from simple task, particularly as cosmic radiation can affect the electron displacement. Besides, one must, of course, make sure that the samples are not accidentally "unfrozen", if only for a brief period, before the actual investigation. As soon as they have been extracted, the samples must be placed in a refrigerator and kept there until required for the test. Rock samples, examined by Zeller, showed that in the locations where they had been extracted an Antarctic Ice Age had kept them cold and "frozen" for 170,000 years.

It appears likely that this electron rock clock can be improved so as not only to yield in the future more accurate age determinations but also make dating of shorter time periods possible. Archaeologists are beginning to show an interest in this method. Supposing a pottery vessel is fired; the thermoluminescence of the clay would certainly be reduced to zero. If thermoluminescence is found on heating the potsherds the energy thus released would have been stored in the clay since the date of its firing and would correspond to the time interval which has passed since that date.

In any case, we hope that Zeller's method proves of value in the Antarctic, and helps to solve the puzzle of its past.

The International Geophysical Year came to an end on December 31st, 1958. Research groups of no fewer than sixty-seven nations participated in its work. Twelve nations shared the exploration of the Antarctic, and the lion's share was taken by Argentina, Chile, Great Britain, the United States and the Soviet Union. Most of these nations decided to continue the work after 1958 by maintaining Antarctic stations. This shows that valuable results have been obtained and that the governments are planning further important researches.

CHAPTER 15

A PLAÑET'S REALM

Interchange with the universe. Mysterious moonscapes. Flight
of the automatic interplanetary station. Two belts surround
the earth. Poor prospects for astronauts. Experiments in the
magnetosphere. Death of the satellites.

THE earth is a planet of the sun. That is an axiom known to
every schoolboy, but its meaning is not always clear. In the
physics laboratory at school there was a mechanical model of
the planetary system: a small, greyish-green ball, the earth,
circled at an angle round a large golden sun. We tried to
imagine ourselves as living on this tiny ball.

This simple picture is misleading. It is always a good idea to
survey an object of interest from a distance. Let us, therefore,
travel in imagination to the nearest celestial body—the moon.
It seems a long way, a distance of 240,000 miles is difficult to
imagine. Even the earth's circumference of roughly 24,000
miles is hard to grasp. There is no regular rocket service to the
moon yet and if we travelled by cannon ball like Baron Munch-
hausen we should need a fortnight, and walking that distance
would take twenty-seven years. But, no matter how we got
there, we should have reached a very good observation post for
our earth.

The idea of projecting ourselves to the moon is not new, not
a feature of the rocket age. Kepler was so familiar with the idea
in 1620 that he wrote a dream-fantasy called *Somnium*, in which
he described the inhabitants of the moon, their buildings, their
plants and animals. His imaginative description of the world as
seen from the moon, however, is exact in every detail: the sky,
the motions of the sun, the earth and the planets, the alternation
of day and night, and of heat and cold.

Let us assume that we have just arrived on the moon. The
full earth hangs over us, four times the size of the familiar moon,
an overwhelming, even alarming sight. With the naked eye
we can discern continents, oceans, peninsulas and bays. With a
telescope we could even see towns, provided there were no
intervening clouds.

These clouds belong to the earth, but we do not know where the most tenuous vapour drifts end, i.e., where the earth ends and cosmic space begins. Should we say that the earth ends where men can no longer live without auxiliary devices? This would introduce a "breathing-sphere" instead of an atmosphere, and such a delimitation of about 4 miles above the earth's surface is surely wrong. It is true that about 90 per cent of the earth's atmosphere lies close to the earth, less than 10 miles from its surface, and if we consider an envelope round the earth of under 20 miles, 99 per cent of the earth's gaseous surroundings are included in it. Even if we estimate the depth of the earth's atmosphere at 80 miles, there will still be a fraction of "atmospheric" gas beyond it. It is obvious that gaseous particles which really belong to the earth escape continuously into cosmic space.

Interchange with the universe

Hydrogen atoms, the lightest of all gas particles, are least subject to the earth's force of attraction and are most likely to leave the earth's field of gravitation. Heavy gases respond to gravity to a greater degree. This is proved by their absence from the air at great altitudes. It is clear that a gas particle which, by diffusion, has drifted far away from the earth is subject to very little gravity. It is clear, therefore, that there is a genuine difficulty in determining the extent of the earth's gas envelope.

The situation is complicated by a second factor. Cosmic space is not empty, and the earth captures substances from space.

The cosmic rays which reach us consist primarily of hydrogen nuclei, i.e., protons. For every hundred hydrogen nuclei there are about ten helium nuclei and one "heavy" nucleus, generally carbon, nitrogen or oxygen. In addition, minute quantities of various other chemical elements reach the earth, such as iron, nickel, lithium, beryllium, boron, etc. The earth captures the atoms of many elements, the cosmic presence of which we know from the spectrum analysis of starlight.

To give an idea of the order of magnitude with which geophysicists are concerned, the so-called solar wind should be mentioned. This term describes the stream of particles, mostly protons, i.e., atomic nuclei of hydrogen, which the sun emits into space. It is now known how much solar wind issues from the sun, and how far the earth is from the sun, and we can therefore estimate to what distance the earth's magnetic field is powerful enough to capture the solar particles. The result of this estimate is remarkable; the earth captures no less than 1·6 tons of matter per second from the solar wind. If this acquisition of matter has continued for 3,300 million years, a reasonable estimate in view of the age of the earth, the latter has received so much hydrogen that, after combining with oxygen to form water, there would be more than enough water to fill all the oceans.

A much smaller acquisition of matter by the earth occurs when the latter passes through the tail of a comet. A comet consists of gases and meteoric dust, and may stretch over many million miles. A comet "head" is only a few miles in diameter, and consists of fairly loose agglomerations of meteoric matter and frozen gases.

If we add together the above-mentioned acquisitions of mass by the earth, including the continuous settling of cosmic dust, we find that the earth grows in weight annually by many million tons. There are even indications that at an altitude of less than 2,000 miles the earth is surrounded by a dust layer.

The radiated energy received by the earth, and the heat which escapes from the earth, follow a similar pattern. Each ray of sunshine received by the earth can be recorded as an asset, but in turn the earth radiates considerable amounts of heat and light back into space.

These are not the only energies, however, which the earth has at its disposal. We have only to think of the gravitational forces which keep the earth and the moon together. The oceans would be several degrees colder if the energy of ebb and flow did not raise their temperature.

Even this brief and incomplete list makes one thing clear. The earth and outer space interact, and we are incapable of determining whether a particle which we might enounter in space, far from the solid surface of the earth, should be described as part of the earth or belonging to space.

In the past few years mankind has started to make its own contribution to blurring the borders between the earth and space by penetrating space with rockets, and by sending probes into space. With every space probe which does not return to earth we irrevocably lose some terrestrial matter and energy. Whenever we fire a rocket, an equivalent high pressure acts in the opposite direction towards the earth. Strictly speaking, the unit earth + space probe becomes two celestial bodies. We have for a long time been accustomed to the opposite process, the blending of the earth and an incoming celestial body. Just as the impact of a meteorite gives the earth a push, so does the launching of a rocket affect the earth too. Both these effects are, of course, infinitely small compared with the orbit of the earth round the sun, or the rotation of the earth about its axis.

The earth is not the sharply defined solid sphere which we see in a model. It is an area, a spatial concept, in the solar system and the universe. It has no fixed place, no definite boundaries, and yet it serves to house our own "world".

Mysterious moonscapes

The moon, to which we have travelled in imagination, has for some time been a target of scientific research. Strangely enough, we know very little about our nearest neighbour, which is chained to us by the forces of gravity. Moreover, our moon is a cosmic freak; it is much too big for its parent planet—the earth. There are many excellent photographs of the face which the moon turns to us. We can see light and dark areas on it, mountain ranges, valleys and huge craters, as of volcanoes. In places the surface of the moon appears to be covered with streaks of light. On large-scale photographs we can see fine crevices, ravines and cracks. The photographs have been meticulously and repeatedly examined, but we still cannot see enough to "understand" them. Giant telescopes, such as that on Mount Palomar, are not really suitable for taking moon photographs. Their magnification is so great that the movements of the earth's atmosphere cause interference in photographing such a "near" object as the moon.

In 1942 the first atomic reactor was built in the crenellated sports stadium of Chicago, where a bronze plaque now commemorates the event. Diagonally opposite this plaque is the entrance to the Enrico Fermi Institute for Nuclear Studies, where a distinguished group of nuclear research scientists worked during the war. Prominent among them was Harold C. Urey, who received the Nobel Prize for Physics in 1934 for the discovery of heavy hydrogen, called deuterium. Like so many physicists and engineers who, in the past as today, in their joy in, and enthusiam for their work unintentionally created the most horrifying weapons, Urey is an idealist. He is a family man, attached to his home and taking pleasure in his garden.

In spite of the award of high honours, Urey withdrew disillusioned from nuclear-weapon work at the end of the war; he had dreamt of a sensible world government and not of wholesale murder. He looked for a new field of activity. There were two problems which attracted him: how life on earth began, and how the moon originated or, rather, how its surface was formed. Just after the end of the war, when Urey began to take an interest in the moon, the latter, considered as a research target, was a completely peaceful objective. The origin, the surface and various properties of the moon were of purely academic interest, and of no concern either to the politicians or the military. Today, we are no longer so sure about that. Will Urey experience a repetition of his tragic disappointment? It seems that the most peace-loving scientist cannot carry on his work without destructive powers moving in to exploit the results.

When Urey started his new line of research he had nothing to go on except two photographs, each showing one half of the moon. These were taken for him under the most favourable conditions, at half moon. Urey measured and made calculations.

The diameter of the moon is 2,160 miles, that of the earth 7,900 (7,927) miles. The distance from the earth to the moon is 240,000 miles. The moon's average density, its specific weight, is 3·34. These values are known, but not the age of the moon. At a guess, it is as old as the earth. The next question is trickier: was the moon originally hot? Now it is cold, of course. Urey calculated how much heat a globe like the moon, without protective clouds, without an atmosphere, could lose in the course of millions of years, and was forced to an unexpected conclusion: the moon cannot ever have been hot. It was cold throughout the process of its formation. After reaching this conclusion, Urey found that K. G. Gilbert, another scientist, had reached the self-same conclusion in 1892.

The moon has a number of peculiarities which support Urey's conclusion. Like the earth, it is thicker round the equator than a perfect sphere, and flattened at the poles. This difference is very great on earth, because the rapid rotation, once in every twenty-four hours, renders the centrifugal force very strong. In view of the slow rotation of the moon, once in every twenty-eight days, and in view of its mass, the difference in diameters at the poles and the equator should be about 165 feet. The difference, however, is ⅝ mile. The moon has a bulge on the side facing the earth, due to the latter's gravitational forces. If this bulge were 130 feet thick it would be theoretically correct. However, the difference is again ⅝ mile. Both these deviations can be explained if we assume that the moon was at some time nearer to the earth and rotated faster. There is even an hypothesis that the moon is a piece of terrestrial matter which broke away from where the Pacific Ocean now is. If the moon was at some stage fiery-liquid the deformations of its young days would have been smoothed out. It will be the task of the first moon explorers to ascertain whether the interior of the moon is of a "currant bun" structure, i.e., consisting of agglutinated individual particles, indicating its formation from solid matter, or has a heavy core, indicating a former liquid state.

Where do the craters on the moon come from? If the moon has always been cold there can have been no volcanic eruptions. Did gas bubbles rise from the interior, forming blisters, covered with loose dust layers, which later burst? Gilbert considered the question in 1893. He assumed that the craters arose from collisions with other celestial bodies. This theory was neglected by later scientists, but Urey, the physicist, was determined to find out if Gilbert's theory was tenable.

The huge crater of Mare Imbrium shows as a large, dark plain on the lower part of the moon. Any celestial body which could have caused such a crater must have been big and travelling fast. There is a certain unevenness in the Mare Imbrium, and the almost circular crater has a kind of dent in one place. If this is regarded as the point of impact the diameter of the unknown celestial traveller must have been about 125 miles. Urey calculated that, with a density of 3·5, and the probable velocity of 1½ miles per second, the impinging body would have released huge energies on impact, viz., the staggering value was calculated as $4·15.10^{32}$ erg, i.e., the energy of 460,000 million nuclear bombs. This idea did not seem credible. By comparison it would have meant a nuclear bomb explosion on every quarter of an acre of our earth. We cannot even imagine the results of such a catastrophe. Whole regions of the moon would have been disrupted and reduced to fine sand. Large rocks would have been split and hurled far away from the original position. Even if the mass of the colliding body had been distributed evenly over the surface of the moon, it would have resulted in a layer 365 feet deep. If it contained 1 per cent of water, a very doubtful eventuality, the moon would have been covered by a temporary layer of water 13 feet deep.

Will the first moon rockets really get smothered in a thick layer of dust? There are two arguments in favour of the theory that the surface of the moon consists of a layer of dust. One is the manner in which short radio waves are reflected from the surface. Secondly, there are a Soviet astronomer's observations of volcanic activity. This may have been the result of erupting gases which whirled up a fountain of dust.

Could it be true that at a depth of about 100 feet the moon rocks contain an approximately 2,500-foot-deep layer of ice crystals? This is a conclusion drawn by some people in the United States from the reflection of radiotelescope signals. It is possible, for a 100-foot-thick blanket would have cut down considerably the evaporation of any water resources on the moon. Is more water beneath the ice layer? We do not know. Astronauts would certainly greatly appreciate the existence of water in some form or other on the moon.

Flight of the automatic interplanetary station

There are still many unsolved mysteries about the moon. If the light "rays" which come from some craters are, as some say, strips of light-coloured raised soil, why do they not pass through the centre of the crater but pass just off it? What is the origin of the strange, jagged cracks, which look as if a snowball had been rolled over a stretch of virgin snow? How can we explain the strictly oriented, sometimes parallel, ridges of some lunar mountain ranges?

Is there really a "tunnel" on the moon? On one of the mountain plateaux there are two lighter spots. If we continue looking along the same direction beyond them there is a long, narrow, white strip. Did a tangential meteorite sweep along the surface, break through the plateau and throw up moon dust?

The recent guesses and theories about the moon show how little we really know about it. Some say that the moon once had an atmosphere, just like the earth, and that there was water, too. Some even go so far as to wonder if life existed on the moon at that time, taking into consideration that life started on earth 2,600 million years ago, and that comparable conditions existed on the moon for a thousand million years.

The photographs of the other side of the moon, taken by a Soviet satellite, have not helped to solve the moon's mysteries.

A fragment of the Xiquipilco, Mexico, iron meteorite, weighing about 24 oz and showing the Widmanstätten etched patterns. The internal fine structure of iron meteorites is named after A. v. Widmanstätten, Director of the Fabrik.-Produkten-Cabinett in Vienna

A slice of the Potter meteorite, Nebraska, U.S.A., weighing just under 5 oz, a stone meteorite of mixed composition

North Africa, photographed by Captain John Glenn during his orbital flight on
February 20th, 1962, with a 35-mm film camera. The deep shadows are those of
the Atlas Mountains

A rainbow-like sunset, photographed by Captain John Glenn during his orbital
flight on February 20th, 1962. He described the colours as brilliant. The orange
line of the horizon shades into blue and then becomes almost black. The photograph was taken from the porthole of the space capsule with an ordinary camera

Those who believed that the other side of the moon would turn out to be broadly similar to the visible side have been disappointed. There are hardly any big craters, but inummerable small, ring-shaped mounds of various sizes, and a mountain range, now named the "Soviet Mountains", running in an almost perfect north–south direction. We have no solution to the problem of the origin of this other moonscape. We can only hope that future years may answer at least some of the questions. Perhaps it would be enough to land a spectroanalyser on the moon. The data transmitted from it would put a solid base under our scattered bits of knowledge.

The technical difficulties of getting an instrument to the moon are enormous, but the automatic interplanetary station which photographed the back of the moon has demonstrated that physical experiments of great accuracy are possible in space. The Soviet interplanetary station was 52 inches long, without aerials, and 48 inches in diameter. It was shot into a carefully calculated orbit. On the third day it reached the moon's gravitational field and was turned from its course in such a way as to fly round the back of the moon.

Several automatic processes took place in the station on the way out. The temperature had to be kept below 77° F in order to ensure the faultless operation of the instruments and the power supply. The space probe was therefore fitted with a device which dimmed the sunlight by venetian blinds and added or dissipated heat as necessary. When the station approached to within 37,500–43,700 miles of the moon the orientating system had to be started. At that time three bright celestial bodies were shining on the station: the sun, the earth and the moon. To direct the station towards the moon its rotation was stopped. The solar direction-finder was then put into operation in order to turn the base of the probe towards the sun.

The photographic camera was then pointed at the moon. It had two objectives, one with a focus of 8 inches and an aperture of 1 : 5·6, the other with a focus of 20 inches and an aperture of 1 : 9·6. The first objective could cover the whole of the moon, the second a fraction of it on an enlarged scale. After the probe had been stabilised in space the solar orientating device was switched off, and a test was made by a special lunar orientating device to ensure that the moon was really in front of the camera. Then a shutter opened automatically in the upper part of the base and exposed the film. The lunar orientating device ensured the steady orientation of the interplanetary station towards the moon for as long as the camera was photographing the back of it, i.e., for about 40 minutes. The exposure time was automatically reset over a range of values during the series of takes, in order to ensure at least some pictures with optimum timing. The special film used in the camera could be developed in hot temperatures. Special anti-radiation measures had been taken

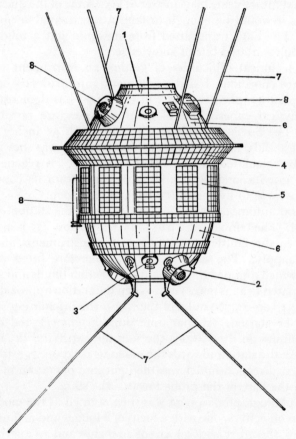

Diagram of the Automatic Interplanetary Station
1. Aperture for camera.
2. Orientation system mechanism.
3. Photoelectric cells for solar orientation
4. Solar battery
5. Shutters for temperature control
6. Heat shield
7. Antennas
8. Unspecified scientific instruments

to prevent the film being fogged by cosmic rays and so rendered useless for accurate reproduction. An unfavourable circumstance was the fact that, from the camera's viewpoint, the sun's rays were vertical to the surface of the moon, and therefore the Soviet photographs of the back of the moon lack the sharp contrasts and shadows which we usually see in lunar photographs.

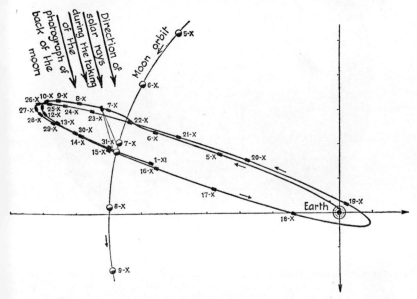

Path of the Soviet Interplanetary Station from its launching up to November 1st, 1959. The positions of the station are marked along its orbit, and the illumination of the moon is indicated

The path of the automatic interplanetary station brought it to just under 5,000 miles from the centre of the moon. It had been planned to direct the space station south of the moon at the point of nearest approach. As a result of the gravitational forces of the moon, the station would veer north. Its greatest distance from the earth was 300,000 miles. When it finally approached the earth again it could be observed from the earth's northern hemisphere as a non-setting star. It travelled back for several days along a long elliptical orbit until it came within nearly 30,000 miles of the earth at its nearest approach.

Then the last stage of the venture began. The film had been automatically developed in the satellite, fixed, dried and rolled round a special transmission cylinder. By means of radio signals sent out to the space station, which had begun rotating again

163

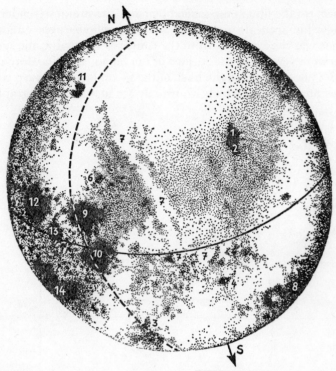

The reverse side of the moon. The semicircular line drawn from left to right is the lunar equator. The dotted line from top to bottom marks the boundary between the visible (*left*) and the reverse side of the moon

1. Mare Moscovianum, a crater 187 miles in diameter
2. Mare Austronautarum in the Mare Moscovianum; south of it, near the lunar equator, the dark patch of the Mare Mendelevianum
3. Mare Australis, continues on the reverse side of the moon
4. Tsiolkovsky Crater with central mountain
5. Lomonosov Crater
6. Joliot-Curie Crater
7. Sovietsky Ridge
8. Mare Somnium
9. Mare Marginis, and
10. Mare Smithii, continue on the reverse side
11. Mare Humboldtianum
12. Mare Crisium
13. Mare Undarum
14. Mare Fecunditatis

after taking the moon photograph, the power sources for the television transmitter on board were started. Then the developed film, appropriately illuminated, was slowly passed before a television camera. The camera's record of the film was transformed into radio pulses and transmitted to earth. As the whole trip of the station took a fortnight, emergency radio transmission equipment and the power sources had been built into the probe as a reserve. In spite of all this, the observation posts on earth received only rather weak signals. The information had therefore to be transmitted very slowly in order to lower the interference level.

The radio signals were recorded in four ways:

(1) on film;
(2) on magnetic recording tape;
(3) by means of special television valves with prolonged afterglow;
(4) by a special electrochemical process on paper.

The greatest distance from which pictures were received from the space probe was 292,000 miles.

According to the information published, the station remained in its planned orbit from the time of its launching on October 4th, 1959, until March, 1960. During that period it circled the earth eleven times. It was not possible to guide the station back to earth and land it, but though the moon is a very close neighbour as cosmic distances go, the flight was an outstanding technical and scientific achievement. A crewless space-ship travelled close to another celestial body and returned towards its launching planet, thus linking two celestial bodies for the first time.

It is not known whether the Soviet space station tried to take photographs from space of the earth as well, during its outward or return flight. Technically this would certainly have been possible. In any case, we hope that Kepler's dream of seeing the earth and the stars from the moon will soon come true.

Two belts surround the earth

We have noted how indefinite is the boundary between the earth and outer space, and how much matter the earth captures from the universe, and particularly from the sun. The earth's magnetic field plays a predominant part in this process. Fifty years ago a Norwegian scientist suggested the possibility that the magnetic lines of force enveloped the earth exactly as they did for any other type of magnet.

We saw in the chapter on continental drift how these lines stretch from pole to pole. They are parallel to the earth's surface, and less close to each other across the earth's magnetic equator, but at the magnetic poles they converge and are strongly bent towards the earth. It is common knowledge that electrically charged particles can move in a spiral along magnetic field lines. Charged particles, e.g., electrons, oscillate along the lines of force from pole to pole in a spiral motion for some considerable time, until they can escape from their magnetic cage at one of the poles. When they do, we can see them as aurorae, shining at the boundary of the earth's atmosphere. It has been known for some time that, after gaseous eruptions on the sun, aurorae, or northern lights, become visible in large numbers, apparently because the geomagnetic field is incapable of retaining all the charged particles emitted by the sun. In 1938, during a sunspot maximum, northern lights were seen even in Germany, i.e., very far south of the magnetic pole.

It is clear that vast amounts of energy are involved in these phenomena. Nevertheless, the actual discovery of a magnetic belt came as a surprise. On February 1st, 1958, the American satellite Explorer I was launched. It circled the earth every 106·7 minutes, its altitude fluctuating between 217 and 731 miles. It transmitted regularly the values obtained by its radiation counter. There was only one thing wrong with these measurements: occasionally the counter stopped functioning. There were suggestions about its being faulty, or damaged by the launching of the space probe. An alternative was the supposition of radiation-free areas.

Nobody could think of a satisfactory explanation at Iowa University, where J. A. Van Allen, with a group of physicists, processed the measurements. Most of the results were more or less what the scientists expected, but the blanks on the radiation counter records were inexplicable.

The solution of the puzzle proved to be less difficult than was expected after the first shock of surprise. A radiation counter can only count the particles one after the other. In other words, if the change in the charge caused inside the counter has not balanced out before the next particle arrives, the latter leaves no record. The second particle, or rather the second radiation unit, hits the counter during the latter's "dead period". This was what had happened in this case. The gaps did not arise from the satellite flying through radiation-free space, but through areas where the counter was overloaded.

On May 1st, 1958, Van Allen read a paper on this phenomenon at a meeting of the National Academy of Sciences of the United States, and the enthusiasm about his discovery was so great that the area of this radiation was called the Van Allen belt, for it stretches like a broad belt round the equatorial area of the earth. In August, 1958, Soviet scientists announced, as part of the International Geophysical Year communications, that their sputnik had also observed the Van Allen belt radiations.

Poor prospects for astronauts

The discovery of the Van Allen radiation belt presented future space travellers with an unexpected hazard, for it would

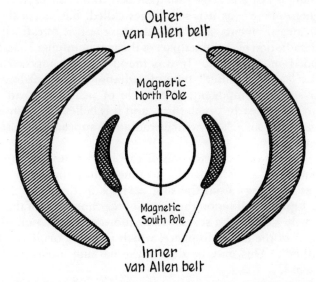

Diagram of the earth with the two Van Allen radiation belts

not do to expose a man to the dangers of this intense radiation. He had already to face the risk of solar eruptions, as was shown by Discoverer XVII, which returned contaminated with radio-activity, and it is impossible to tell beforehand when the sun will be likely to emit clouds of gases.

It has been calculated that the Van Allen belt is scarcely thicker than 1,875 miles, and therefore a space-ship would travel through it fairly quickly. Moreover, it could be protected to a certain extent against radiation. It was therefore believed that the radiation belt would present no insuperable obstacle to space travellers.

These hopes collapsed when the measuring instruments of the

space probe Pioneer III, which came down to earth after reaching an altitude of 68,700 miles, were examined. They showed the existence of another Van Allen belt farther out in space. The distances of the two belts from the earth are 8,125 and 15,625 miles respectively.

In August, 1961, Explorer XII was launched. The altitude of its orbit fluctuated between 169 and nearly 50,000 miles. The records of the physics laboratory mounted inside it supplemented our previous knowledge. Presumably there is no sharp division between the two radiation belts. It is quite possible that there is just one large radiation belt round the earth. This "magnetosphere", as it is sometimes called, has, according to earlier measurements, a certain structure and is "stratified".

The radiation of the inner part of the magnetosphere has been examined more closely. It was found to be composed of a "harder" and a "softer" type of radiation. The harder, i.e., higher-energy component, is capable of penetrating an aluminium sheet nearly $\frac{1}{2}$ inch thick, and it is believed to consist of protons. The softer and weaker radiation appears to consist of electrons.

The details of the formation of this magnetosphere are still unknown, but it is generally assumed that the outer layer receives its energy from the sun, perhaps in the form of solar wind. Opinions differ on the origin of the inner part of the Van Allen belt. There are several indications of fluctuation in the diameter of the magnetosphere, which pulsates, or, if you like, "breathes". This may be due to the varying intensity of the solar wind.

There is, however, general agreement that space flight through the two belts is out of the question. The protective shields required to safeguard the pilot would be too heavy. The magnetic pole regions of the earth will therefore be the only areas suitable as launching and, we hope, landing places for space flights, and even then only in years of statistically low solar activity.

Experiments in the magnetosphere

Our knowledge of the magnetosphere is still very scanty. The information we have about the connection between gaseous eruptions in the sun and so-called magnetic storms, or any changes in the magnetic field strength of our planet, is very inadequate. Experimental investigations of the properties of the radiation belt round the earth began in 1958, but it is difficult to determine whether they were planned or purely empirical at the time. In August, 1958, American scientists exploded three small nuclear bombs at a considerable altitude (Project Argus). The resultant extraordinary air glow was observed in Saskatoon, Canada. It indicated that abnormally large quantities of the alkaline metal lithium were present at high altitudes. From this experts were able to conclude that the explosions were due to hydrogen bombs which produce lithium in the course of their thermonuclear reaction. A spectacular aurora was also observed at that time, and indicated that the explosion had released into the magnetic field of the earth electrons which ultimately reached the polar regions in their travel along the earth's cage of magnetic lines of force.

We do not know whether, or to what extent, subsequent Soviet explosions influenced the magnetosphere, but we may assume that the two biggest Soviet bombs, tested at the end of October, 1961 produced considerable amounts of lithium at high altitudes, because an abnormal air glow was again recorded at Saskatoon.

Many scientists raised their voices in warning, asking whether such disturbances of the magnetosphere might not have harmful consequences for our planet. Some such assumption appears justified, and climatic changes seem a possible consequence.

Military circles in the United States pressed for more high-altitude bomb tests. It had been known for a long time that radio interference was connected with the appearance of aurorae. The question was whether high-altitude explosions might put out of action the radio system of the American early warning defence system.

After several unsuccessful attempts, the Americans managed to explode a large atomic bomb at an altitude of about 200 miles near Johnston Island (16·7° N, 165·5° W) at 09.00 hours and 15 seconds international time on July 9th, 1962. During that night observers in Honolulu, 750 miles away, saw a grand spectacle. First there was a bright white flash, followed by an intense green light which, five seconds later, turned into a pink glow, fading gradually into sunset colours during the course of six or seven minutes before it disappeared altogether.

The time of the explosion was carefully chosen. On July 29th, 1961, a special satellite, called Injun I, had been put into a 104-minute orbit varying in altitude from 556 to 631 miles.

This satellite was equipped with three special radiation counters which, before the explosion, regularly transmitted the condition existing in the lower part of the Van Allen belt, viz., a flux of between 700 and 1,200 electrons and protons per second. At the moment of the explosion Injun I was at an altitude of 554 miles on a NE course over the Pacific, heading for Canada. In other words, the seat of the explosion was immediately in its rear. Forty-five minutes later, Injun I passed Southern Rhodesia, when it transmitted a series of extraordinarily high radiation values, i.e., instead of about 1,000 particles per second it recorded more than 11,000 per second. This record of radiation an hour after the explosion permitted an estimate to be made of the additional electrons in the geomagnetic field. These amounted to 10^{24}. In places near the earth, where usually one particle per second had been recorded, the estimate now was 100 particles per second, of such high energy that they were able to penetrate the lead shields of the counters. A radiation belt of unexpected intensity had been created round the earth reaching down to an altitude of only 275 miles.

Injun I was not the only satellite, however, which was in a favourable recording position at the time of the explosion. The joint Anglo-American satellite Ariel, launched on April 26th, 1962, and circling the earth in an orbit varying in altitude from 246 to 756 miles, was also equipped to record radiation with its Geiger–Müller counter and a special cosmic-ray counter enclosed in a thin lead casing. For months these counters had functioned perfectly. At the moment of the explosion on July 9th, 1962, over Johnston Island, Ariel was 925 miles south of that point on a course which would take it over Central America, i.e., it had to pass eastward of the site of the explosion. Twenty seconds after the explosion, Ariel's counters began to record increased radiation which reached a hitherto unrecorded maximum two minutes later. This was something new and unexpected; the disturbance of the geomagnetic field by the explosion had travelled at almost incredible speed. The entire magnetosphere had been affected. Eight minutes later the radiation again became so strong that the limit of the measuring and recording capacity of Ariel's instruments was reached, and Ariel continued to record this maximum until it reached the North Atlantic. Its subsequent orbits took Ariel nearer and nearer to Johnston Island, and therefore it is understandable that the recording curve of its radiation counters see-sawed wildly.

Two events shown up by the records were outstanding: (i) the electrons projected into the geomagnetic field formed a radiation belt round the earth in twenty minutes; and (ii) the area between the latitudes 20° north and 20° south of the equator had the greatest radioactivity. The electrons resulting from the explosion of July 9th, 1962, had been projected into the magnetosphere up to a distance of 18,750 miles.

By July 12th, 1962, the radiation intensity had decreased considerably, but it is still impossible to say for certain how long the radiation belt will remain active.

Death of the satellites

The strength, the high energies and the hazards of the intensified radiation belt were nowhere shown more clearly than in their effect on the functioning of satellites. Ariel, the chief witness of the experiment, was the first satellite that died. Its electronic heart stopped, and its messages quickly became fragmentary. On July 13th, four days after the explosion, its transmission system broke down completely. The unexpected had occurred; the solar cells which supplied power to the satellite had been rendered useless by the strong radiation. Injun I was not much better off. Its functioning was seriously impaired, and only the lead-shielded central counter transmitted information about the new radiation belt for a little while longer.

Two probes, Transit IVb and Traac, were launched on November 15th, 1961, and went into orbit together. They were intended mainly for navigation experiments. The charged particles of the new radiation belt destroyed their solar cells too, and inactivated their transmitters. For another month the smaller probe Traac transmitted what it managed to record by means of a lead-shielded counter, and then gave up.

Telstar, the television and communications satellite of the Bell Telephone Laboratories, transmitted some information on various radiation areas up to a height of 2,750 miles, but its solar cells too suffered severely.

It is very probable that some American military observation stations have suffered the same fate. So far the investigation of the earth's radiation belt has been a tragic story of unmanned probes sacrificed to a strategic experiment in ignorance of its consequences.

The new radiation belt is a still greater danger for manned space flight than the natural radiation regions of the earth's magnetosphere. Manned space flight will scarcely be possible beyond an altitude of 156 miles. It will have to be restricted to the "Gagarin route", a narrow zone between the denser part of the atmosphere and the radiation belts. At an altitude of from 80 to 90 miles the air resistance is small enough to exert negligible braking power on space-ships. The flights of the Soviet space-ships Vostok III and Vostok IV have demonstrated the degree of precision required to maintain the most favourable flight path and the certainty with which this can be done. Vostok III travelled at a speed of 7,821 metres per second at an altitude of 114 miles; Vostok IV had a speed of 7,824 metres per second at an altitude of 113 miles. The speed of these two ships was therefore kept equal to within 3 metres per second, an astounding performance in view of their actual flight velocity. If a rocket takes a space capsule up to about 113 miles and the latter has a flight velocity of only 5 per cent short of the critical orbiting velocity it would fall back to the ground without circling the earth even once.

There can therefore be no doubt that the increased radiation of the magnetosphere presents a serious obstacle to manned space flights until the radiation intensity drops to its normal level. On the other hand, our present knowledge of the earth's radiation belts entitles us to state that outer space, i.e., the region beyond any influence created by the earth, begins at about 50,000 miles, well outside the earth's magnetosphere.

IV

Let the earth bring forth the living creature
after his kind.

Genesis I. 24

In Genesis the origin of life is divided into three phases. On the third day of creation plants were created. On the fifth day marine animals and birds appeared. The sixth day produced land animals, and lastly came man.

What do we know today about the origin of life? We are still unable to create life synthetically in a test-tube, and it is doubtful whether it will ever be possible, because what we call "life" is a highly developed form of existence. In trying to reproduce it we are entering into competition with ourselves, for we try to create, not just any sort of life, but conscious, sentient life, and would be satisfied only if we could synthetically create creatures more perfect than ourselves. Such notions, however, do not help us.

Experiments which showed that the origin of life on earth was no accident, but a process which was apparently inevitable and a result of natural laws, opened more fruitful lines of investigation. A complete absence of life would be much more astonishing than its existence. If, however, the origin of life is the result of natural laws the question arises where, apart from our own planet, conditions exist which have made, or will make, the appearance of some kind of life possible.

CHAPTER 16

AND THE EARTH WAS WITHOUT FORM AND VOID

Kant's error. Weizsäcker's turbulence theory. Our earth is only a remnant. Origin of oxygen in the atmosphere.

THERE appears to be an important, even essential, gap in the Bible story of creation. Nothing is said about the creation of gases before the various forms of life. Not even air is mentioned, which is surprising, for the importance of the atmosphere for the origin of higher forms of life could not have escaped the careful chroniclers of Genesis. Perhaps they took it for granted. Not until the second chapter of the First Book of Genesis is the "living breath" mentioned.

It seems that there is an unbridgeable gap in the progress of events, but actually the very opposite is the case. With admirable assurance the first verses of the Bible postulate a preliminary stage—"heaven", apparently an amorphous stage of diffuse material for creation. This is exactly the condition which the scientists always had to assume when they attempted to explain the formation of our planetary system, and such attempts were many.

The planets have always been the favourite and most interesting subject in astronomy. Some knowledge about their motion, their sizes and their distances from the sun had long been available. Any theory of the origin of our planetary system had to try to fit these observational data.

For instance, there exists a law governing our planetary system which requires explanation. As long ago as 1837 Arago presented this law in the form of a "crib":

"Write the following figures in a line so that the rule governing their progression becomes clear—

0, 3, 6, 12, 24, 48, 96, 192;

if 4 is added to each of these figures, we get—

4, 7, 10, 16, 28, 52, 100, 196",

which, as the author proudly stated, gives the distances of the planets from the sun, if the distance between the earth and the sun is taken as 10. In actual fact this rule is pretty accurate, as is shown in the following table:

	Arago's figures	Today's value
Mercury	4	3·87
Venus	7	7·23
Earth	10	10
Mars	16	15·24
Asteroids	28	27
Jupiter	52	52·03
Saturn	100	95·31
Uranus	196	191·91

This kind of playing with figures renders problems attractive, and therefore not only scientists but also laymen attempted to solve the puzzles of our planetary system. A case in point is Hanns Hoerbiger's "world ice theory", which created a sensation around 1920. Hoerbiger was an excellent mechanical engineer; he even made his mark in the history of engineering by inventing a valve, and his sons Paul and Attila became well-known actors, but his theory proved erroneous.

Kant's error

The oldest attempts at understanding our planetary system had first to explain the rotation of the planets. It seemed reasonable to suppose that their rotation was initiated by an impact. In 1749 George Louis Leclerc, Count Buffon, French scientist and author of a natural history in forty volumes, did not hesitate to assume that the sun had once collided with a huge comet whose tail had pulled quantities of matter from the sun and started these fragments spinning.

This type of origin of the planetary system seems catastrophic and rather ominous. After all, if such an event has happened once it might happen again!

The philosopher Immanuel Kant tried to construct a picture of evolutionary progress. He started out with the idea of a large rotating gas cloud, as large as the whole of our planetary system. He suggested that this cloud gradually cooled and contracted. In this way a central sun originated, rotating ever faster round its axis. Enormous centrifugal forces at its equator caused the splitting off of matter from which the planets were subsequently formed. Pierre Simon, Marquis de Laplace, the French mathematician, took over Kant's idea, developed it further and published it in 1796 in his *Exposition du système du monde*. In the middle of the nineteenth century the basic premisses of this idea were re-examined, and it was found that some aspects could not possibly be correct. For instance, in the Kant–Laplace model the sun would have to rotate about its axis seven times in an hour, while in reality it rotates only once in four weeks. Finally, an attempt was made to string together the most plausible parts of all the earlier speculative explanations and leave it at that.

Weizsäcker's turbulence theory

As late as 1944 it was generally asserted in scientific literature that not one of the theories postulated hitherto about the origin of the planetary system was tenable, "for each one of them was shown to contradict known facts when accurate calculations were made". Bernhard Bavink, the natural philosopher who pronounced the above harsh judgment on the hypotheses of the most prominent scientists and thinkers of past centuries, allowed a certain modicum of probability for only one hypothesis:

"It is doubtful whether the recently widely circulated hypothesis of Jeans is tenable. According to Jeans, the passing of another large star drew from the sun a column of matter which was thin at the start, thickened for a while, and then tapered off, finally dividing into planets. This hypothesis explains to some extent the uneven distribution of mass among the planets, as well as a few other points. It would, however, be rather rash to consider it a final solution of the problem."

When Bavink's book *Achievements of Natural Science* appeared, the problem had found a satisfactory solution for the first time. In the autumn of 1943 Carl Friedrich Weizsäcker, a young German physicist, put forward an explanation, based on the fact that a certain region in space contained traces of interstellar matter, fine dust and gases, e.g., hydrogen. The density of this matter, at first perhaps less than 1 oz in 700 million cubic miles, gradually increased. First the sun with its enveloping gas originated from it, and next the planets were inevitably formed from agglomerations of dust and gas at various distances from the central sun. Mathematically, physically and astronomically, Weizsäcker's theory fits in astonishingly well with the known facts about our solar system; the mass, direction of rotation, the rotation itself and orbital period of the planet.

The most important point about Weizsäcker's turbulence theory, however, is that it was not a special or unique case that he described. The origin of our planetary system is in no way extraordinary. All stars and planetary systems probably originated in the same way. The once attractively simple theory of an impact of a giant meteor or comet on the sun has been superseded. Such a collision would not only be very improbable, it would also fail to provide a satisfactory explanation of the size of the planets, their distances from the sun and their individual rotation. Besides, it would still leave the special case of the origin of our sun without an explanation.

Our earth is only a remnant

We are still unable to estimate what the temperature was when the earth originated. Opinions differ considerably. It is, however, certain that at first there was darkness, for gas and dust clouds hid the sun from view. When dust particles reached the earth's field of attraction they gradually settled. On the other hand, large quantities of gases dispersed into cosmic space. In its early days the earth undoubtedly lost considerable amounts of matter. As a result some chemical elements are now completely, or almost completely, missing from the earth. Originally they were probably present in abundance. For instance, our atmosphere is very poor in rare gases. It may be assumed that the original terrestrial air was rich in hydrogen, which is a very light gas. Hydrogen escaped into space and took large quantities of rare gases with it. It is even possible that at times the earth lost its atmosphere completely. What we observe today is a secondary atmosphere. If we make a rough estimate of the stock of terrestrial hydrogen we find that it corresponds to a quantity which could have been contained in a terrestrial crust 13–20 miles thick, which is the actual thickness of the earth's crust. Today's atmosphere may once have been contained in the earth's crust.

It can be assumed with some degree of certainty that what we consider as the earth today is only a fraction of its original mass. If we compare it with Jupiter we find that the latter's mass is 318 times that of the earth, and its force of attraction correspondingly larger. It consists of 80 per cent hydrogen and

15 per cent of the rare gas helium. In the outer layers of the earth, however, which naturally are most depleted of hydrogen, the latter occurs only in the eighth, or even tenth, place. On the small planet Mars the hydrogen remnant is infinitesimal. Nevertheless, Mars is large enough to retain at least CO_2, a heavy gas, in its atmosphere. The earth is somewhere in the middle, between the two planets mentioned.

If the earth lost much terrestrial matter during the early days of its formation it also gained something new and valuable. As the dust clouds and the gas envelope disappeared, and sunlight reached the surface of the earth, "it was light".

Origin of oxygen in the atmosphere

There is no difficulty in pointing to a number of processes which would cause the earth to be, not just warm, but actually hot over prolonged periods. As the original matter agglomerated, heat arose from compression. Besides, as chemical elements and minerals were forming, they reacted with each other, and this resulted in a considerable amount of additional heat. Heat also results from the decay of radioactive materials. There are indications, however, that this source of heat was not very important in the case of the earth. Finally, until it achieved stability the original matter settled in stages, and this resulted in the release of frictional heat.

How hot did the earth get? The continents consist mainly of granite, with some basic minerals, such as quartz, feldspar and mica. In order to obtain granite on cooling, a temperature of at least 1,830° F is required. It is believed that under the thin, now solid, earth's crust there is a central core which, at least in its outer layer, is fluid.

The temperature of the earth sank slowly, and a solid crust began to form, but this did not mean that our planet settled peacefully. Crevasses split open, gas and molten lava gushed forth, and volcanic forces shook and shaped the earth. Finally, large areas became solid. A new gas envelope replaced the one that was lost. Hydrogen and oxygen combined to form water. Where the temperatures were low enough, water condensed and rains started. In hotter areas water turned into steam, and clouds surrounded the earth.

During volcanic eruptions gases were released, mainly carbon dioxide, methane, sulphurous gases and nitrogen compounds. Water dissolved some mineral salts. Endless rain floods began to erode the rocks. Abysses, troughs and crevasses filled with saline water which soon formed seas.

With the progress of cooling, rain decreased. One process, however, was decisive for the earth: sunlight, and probably also thunderstorms, decomposed quantities of water vapour in the clouds and liberated oxygen, some of which remained in the earth's new atmosphere, while some dissolved in the water of the seas. It was oxygen which made life possible.

CHAPTER 17

THE RANGE OF LIFE

Wöhler dismisses the "Life Force". The oil eaters. Oldest forms of life. Why the Saurians disappeared. Bacteria in salt.

THE desire to create life synthetically is as old as man, and so is the belief that this is possible, if not by science, then by magic. Again and again man has tried to usurp this privilege of the Creator. The witch doctor attempts to bring the dead back to life with spells and ritual dances. Medieval alchemists thought they could create a homunculus by black magic out of a witch's brew, and their elixir of youth was meant to give eternal life. The philosopher's stone, the ultimate goal of the alchemists, was alleged to have life-creating properties. Life is the greatest miracle, and there is no end to the attempts to copy or imitate it.

The belief that there was a spontaneous generation of life, a primeval calling forth of living creatures from organic substances, is very ancient. For instance, it was believed that worms were generated from dung and mice from Nile mud. In A.D. 220 there was even a report of mice the front part of which had already been formed while the rest was still Nile mud.

Aristotle, who for two thousand years was the incontrovertible scientific and philosophical authority, seriously believed that suitable substances were capable of spontaneously producing plants and animals, such as bees, mosquitoes, flies, frogs, etc. Isidore of Seville, the influential writer and educationalist of the early Middle Ages who died in 636, shared this view. There were legends of goose or duck-bearing trees. Hippocrates believed in the generation of parasites from blood and pus. Avicenna, the Mahommedan doctor and philosopher (980–1037), considered it credible that, under propitious conjunctions of the planets, man could be created "from a correct mixture". He reported that on one occasion a half-finished calf fell from the sky during a clap of thunder.

This story was believed up to the sixteenth century. The later Middle Ages did little to correct such nonsensical ideas. Ambroise Paré, one of the founders of modern surgery

(1517–90), held the opinion that parasites originated from rotten human body fluids, and he was not alone in this belief. Even Denis Diderot (1713–84), the great encyclopaedist of the Age of Enlightenment, believed that highly complex animals could be "crystallised" out of the soil.

It would not be tactful to mention those who tenaciously held to the conviction of the reality of spontaneous creation even

The legend of the goose- or duck-growing tree is based on misinterpreted observations. It was not known where the young Arctic geese which appeared near the Scottish and Irish coasts came from. It was assumed that they came from so-called "duck shells" (a crustacean with feathery feet). These duck shells are often found in drift wood, which was then considered to be broken fragments of the duck tree. In spite of some doubts, this belief persisted even in the eighteenth century

after the dawn of the nineteenth century. In spite of their adherence to outmoded beliefs, they were not bad scientists or philosophers.

A general spreading of chemical knowledge in the eighteenth century led to a classification of various substances. It was recognised that some substances occurred in plants as well as animals, while others were found as minerals. Around 1780 chemical compounds were divided into organic and inorganic. Inorganic, i.e., mineral, substances could undoubtedly be created artificially, but this was apparently impossible with organic substances. The statement that organic substances could originate only with the help of the *vis vitalis*, the Life

Force, became axiomatic. What was this Life Force? Was it "life" itself? The belief in the Life Force was so firmly rooted that famous chemists, such as Gay-Lussac and Döbereiner, preferred indulging in fantastic assumptions to admitting that they obtained "organic" substances in their experiments.

Wöhler dismisses the "Life Force"

On July 31st, 1800, Friedrich Wöhler was born at Eschersheim, at that time near, but not yet part of, Frankfurt. His father was in charge of the stables of the Crown Prince of Hessen and later served the Duke of Meiningen as equerry, agricultural adviser and court theatre manager. This strange combination of duties may account for the manifold talents of Wöhler junior.

While still a schoolboy Friedrich Wöhler took an interest in chemistry, physics and mineralogy. When he left school in 1820 to study medicine in Marburg, like his father, he already had several minor chemical discoveries to his credit. At Marburg Wöhler studied under Leopold Gmelin, the famous professor of medicine and chemistry, but he did not attend lectures on chemistry, as, in Gmelin's opinion, they would be a waste of time for him. After taking his medical degree, he sought out other teachers, such as Berzelius, the "pope of chemistry" of that time, who was working in Stockholm. In the autumn of 1824 Wöhler returned to Germany. Several years of teaching at technical schools in Berlin and Kassel were followed in 1836 by an appointment at Göttingen University, where he remained until his death on September 23rd, 1882.

In Wöhler's lifetime the science of chemistry became firmly established. August Wilhelm von Hofmann laid the foundations of the chemistry of tar dyes, and so the basis of a prosperous German dye industry. August Kekulé worked on carbon compounds; Bunsen and Kirchhoff discovered spectrum analysis. New elements were discovered. Wöhler was the first to isolate aluminium. At first he obtained only flakes of a "metallic lustre, white like tin", but in 1845 he wrote from Göttingen to his friend and fellow chemist Justus von Liebig in Giessen: "I found that aluminium can be obtained in the form of molten pellets of the size of a pinhead, quite malleable, white like tin, and soluble in potassium lye, giving off hydrogen."

It was a creative age; successful analyses and syntheses of new substances followed each other in quick succession. There were,

183

of course, mistakes too, even by great scientists such as Liebig, who wrote to Wöhler on June 26th, 1839:

"I have some news of which I hardly dare speak, for I see in my imagination the corners of your mouth turn down scornfully. I discovered a process for crystallising carbon into diamonds from an aqueous solution. You should see the result sparkle in the sunlight. But don't tell anybody."

Luckily Wöhler did not tell, and this "discovery" of Liebig's remained a secret until their correspondence was published in 1888.

Almost immediately after discovering metallic aluminium, Wöhler made the really important discovery of his life. By producing urea in a test-tube he upset the traditional axiom that only the "Life Force" could create organic substances. On February 22nd, 1828, he communicated his discovery to his former teacher Berzelius:

". . . for I cannot, as it were, hold my chemical water any longer, and have to tell you that I can make urea without the help of kidneys, or a dog, or any animal or man. Urea is ammonium isocyanide. . . . I obtained what I supposed to be ammonium cyanide quite easily by treating lead cyanide with caustic ammonia. . . . It crystallised beautifully, a large number of clear-cut rhombic prisms. . . . Suddenly I knew, and there was nothing else to be done except make a comparative analysis between pissed urea manufactured by myself and the (synthetic) cyanide urea. If, and I cannot see it any other way, no other product but urea originated from the degradation of lead cyanide by ammonia, the pissed urea must have exactly the same composition as ammonia cyanide and thus fully explain this apparent paradox."

Until he received the above letter Berzelius was one of the most ardent champions of the "Life Force" theory. He held it to be impossible to obtain organic substances from inorganic, mineral substances. In 1827, a year before Wöhler's discovery, he wrote in his textbook on organic synthesis: "Art cannot combine the elements of inorganic nature in the manner of living Nature. In our experiments we produce only binary compounds and combinations of them."

However, Wöhler's discovery converted Berzelius, and his judgment was authoritative at that time. Enthusiastically he replied to Wöhler: "Verily the Doctor has invented the art of taking the road to immortality. Aluminium and synthetic urea, although two very different substances, will, dear Sir, be entwined as gems in your laurel wreath."

The development of the new science of the chemistry of life substances—biochemistry—began. At first the paths which lead to the creation of substances usually produced by living organisms were still devious and far removed from the natural processes, but today we know how syntheses in the organism occur, and can reconstruct and imitate them.

The oil eaters

What is Life? We could reply obliquely that the end of life is death, that living things must die. That is not a scientific definition, but it contains the important statement that life is a state which is limited in time.

What are the characteristics of life? Metabolism is undoubtedly one of them, and it starts with eating and drinking. All plants and animals ingest and thus receive nourishment. Propagation is another characteristic. Further, we expect a living organism to occupy a finite volume of space, i.e., have a skin of sorts. Usually we are also inclined to expect some sort of sense organs, though in the case of very primitive organisms this is not an essential characteristic. We know of micro-organisms which float in water and obtain their food by enveloping it. They have neither mouths nor stomachs, and certainly no higher organs. In conclusion, living organisms, as far as we know, respond to external stimuli.

A description of life becomes even more vague if we say that living things need warmth, light and air. These are by no means necessary in very primitive forms of life. A large number of bacteria do not require air for life. The same applies to heat. Many organisms can be kept at temperatures far below freezing point without dying. Even plants do not necessarily die at temperatures below the freezing point of water. There are plants which produce or assimilate substances which lower the freezing point of water, and their sap can therefore still circulate at temperatures below freezing point. At the other end of the scale there are micro-organisms which are able to live in hot, almost boiling, water, such as the Yellowstone Park geysers and springs.

The notion of "no life without light" can also be negatived.

The so-called oil bacteria live in oil, hidden in the earth's interior for millennia. They live without light, at comparatively high temperatures and subject to the pressure of thick layers of rock. They "eat" the hydrocarbons of the oil. They manufacture small fragments of long carbon chains. Their appetite is so great that it has been seriously suggested that poor oil wells should be infested with them. In the opinion of those who propose this, the digestive products of the bacteria, i.e., the shorter and more mobile carbon chain remnants, would decrease the viscosity of the oil residue, which could then be pumped out more easily.

Oil bacteria are not the only peculiar feeders. They, at least, feed on carbon compounds. The sulphate-reducing bacteria are satisfied with inorganic chemical food. During periods of sulphur shortage attempts were made in Britain to make their metabolism available for use in sulphur production.

There are also nitrate and nitrite bacteria which require the simplest carbon compounds for life, and derive energy from the transformation of inorganic compounds.

Oldest forms of life

A recent scientific paper contained a remark which may be important in this context. A report on the metabolism of sulphate-reducing bacteria contained a description of bacteria cultures growing in aqueous solutions which contained nothing but simple inorganic salts or merely sulphates. Air had to be rigidly excluded, for it would have killed these bacteria, which are anaerobic, i.e., air would interfere with their life processes. The experimenter came to the conclusion that the various types of sulphate-reducing bacteria were hardly related to each other. In other words, there is a surprisingly great variety of these peculiar creatures. We know that bacteria have existed for many millions of years. If so many varieties of them developed, the environment must originally have been favourable to them. We may therefore assume that the variety of this kind of bacteria arose in a world where the oxygen of the atmosphere played a very subordinate part. Alternatively, the atmosphere may have consisted of sulphuretted hydrogen. The above-mentioned nitrate and nitrite bacteria may have lived in an atmosphere containing ammonia. We can assume that the sulphate-reducing bacteria with their peculiar metabolism are among the oldest forms of life on earth.

It is unlikely that all forms of life arose at the same time. Extremely primitive forms probably originated first. Had the first creature which we can describe as "living" a metabolism, perhaps a more primitive form of the process as we know it today, but still adequate to enable it to live and to propagate?

Primeval organisms could not have been highly differentiated. Compared with them, the sulphate-reducing bacteria are probably quite complex. Animals and plants of today incorporate differentiated growth substances, hormones, vitamins and enzymes, but the early creatures presumably functioned in a more primitive manner. Even today we have plants which do not conform to the general rule. Some absorb the poisonous element selenium, others, like the common horsetail, contain considerable quantities of silicon. Some Mediterranean tunicates absorb the rare mineral vanadium. Are all these creatures survivals of life forms of earlier ages? Further examples may confirm our supposition. Some coal deposits contain comparatively large amounts of germanium. Some fossils contain caesium, thallium and titanium. Were these elements once essential to life, as essential as iodine is today for our thyroid gland hormone? Or are they the residue of an even older kind of plant or animal metabolism?

It may be amusing to speculate whether a completely different kind of life from that known to us existed on earth when its temperature was several hundred degrees higher. Were there gas clouds in which some energy transformation was proceeding, either inside or around the fringe, that made them divide and multiply? Perhaps they descended to the earth's surface, took up "food", rose again, died and disappeared? All this is pure speculation, for we know nothing of such a kind of "life".

Nevertheless, the idea is not totally absurd. Gustav Theodor Fechner, a German philosopher and natural scientist, went even further. He developed a theory of parallels which, he alleged, existed between the life of terrestrial creatures and the stars, particularly the planets. He assumed that planets were higher organisms which had bodily functions corresponding to their size. As a consequence, he believed that planets had souls. His theory obtained hardly any support, although he was otherwise a very sober natural scientist. Perhaps Goethe would have supported it, for on April 11th, 1827, he expressed an even bolder thought to Eckermann: "I imagine the earth with its

187

circle of vapours as a living creature engaged in eternal breathing in and out."

Why the Saurians disappeared

It would be interesting to consider the largest possible size of an animal. We know of minute micro-organisms which are undoubtedly alive. The largest plants on earth today are probably the giant sequoia trees, and the largest animals are whales. In earlier ages, e.g., the Carboniferous, the earth was covered by lush outsize vegetation. There were also the giant reptiles, the saurians. What became of them? Could such large, or even larger, animals develop again?

Soviet scientists have put forward a new theory about the disappearance of the saurians. The dying out of certain animal species had hitherto been attributed to climatic changes, but Soviet scientists have looked elsewhere for the cause. At least five supernovae, i.e., the flaring up of new stars, have been observed in our galaxy in the past millennium. We know that the residual nebulae of the supernova of 1054 contain large amounts of cosmic radiation. Perhaps our sun, and our entire solar system, entered such a region of high radiation in the proximity of a supernova. A rough calculation shows that such an event could easily have happened about ten times during the history of the earth. Therefore there must have been periods when cosmic radiation was ten, or even a hundred, times stronger than it is now. Such an event must have had serious biological and genetic consequences. Short-lived, i.e., quickly propagating organisms, would have been affected less than long-lived animals, who must have suffered a catastrophic decline. There are indications that the mass extermination of the saurians took place at the end of the Cretaceous Age. On the other hand, similar radiation periods may have caused lush vegetation, such as appeared in the Carboniferous Age. Further research is necessary before this theory can be substantiated. It is mentioned here only because it provides an explanation for the disappearance of extraordinarily large animals while smaller ones apparently remained unaffected.

Bacteria in salt

The thought of extremely short-lived organisms is no less fantastic than the past existence of the saurians. We are inclined to allot at least a few days of life to a living creature, but that is not realistic. There are life forms which exist only for a few hours, or even minutes. Their metabolism is very rapid, according to our ideas of time, but their lives may be filled with as many experiences and events as ours. We cannot tell whether the extent of our experience is really greater than that of the short-lived may-fly. We should be extraordinarily careful how we answer the question of how long or how short an individual life can be.

Can an organism become 380 million years old or, rather, can it survive such a period? Dr. Heinz Dombrowski of the Institute of Physical Medicine and Balneology at Bad Nauheim, Federal Germany, maintains that it can. He has found strange things in the mineral water from the Nauheim springs: minute splinters of wood, and even more minute, fragile remnants of micro-organisms. Their excellent state of preservation, and even their very discovery, were surprising. Dombrowski also found that micro-organisms, immured for millions of years in blocks of rock salt, could be revived if placed in favourable conditions.

The idea of breeding live organisms from mineral salts appears quite incredible at first. Dombrowski wondered whether there was a possible contamination by organisms which, in spite of all precautions, had got into the sample in his laboratory. No trouble was too great for him in order to exclude the possibility of such an error. The definite proof of his discovery was provided by an electron-microscope picture showing the micro-organisms inside their rock-salt packing.

They are strange creatures. One of them, called *Pseudomonas halocrenaea*, is a germ which likes high temperatures to grow in. It prefers +113° to +131° F, and is viable even at +203° F. At the other extreme, a temperature of 14° F does not harm it. There is a certain affinity between it and the micro-organisms which live in the water of the Dead Sea, particularly in those regions where the salt content is very high. The organisms preserved in the rock salt were presumably marine creatures too. Subterranean salt-water streams and lakes would have provided a suitable environment for them. Apparently these organisms retain their viability even when enclosed in solid salt.

Dombrowski made further experiments. He completely de-hydrated some brine containing bacteria, so that the salts crystallised. Surprisingly enough, when the crystals were dissolved in a fresh nutrient, micro-organisms revived and multiplied again. They had not lost their viability or fertility by being enclosed in the solid salt. Even so, one is reluctant to accept this extraordinary research result, although there is no question of just a few sporadic lucky experiments. In 138 attempts at breeding bacteria from salt deposits in Permian limestone there were thirty-six cases of failure to find either dead or living bacteria, in forty-one cases only dead bacteria were found, but in sixty-one instances live bacteria could be bred. What is more, it was not always the same type of bacterium. Dombrowski wrote: "One has the impression that the bacterial fauna of the Permian seas have been brought to life."

As far as we know, the temperature of the Permian seas was 113–131° F, and it is surely no coincidence that this happens to be the most favourable temperature for *Pseudomonas halocrenaea*.

The remnants of Permian seas are far below our feet. In many cases they are overlaid by 2,000-foot-thick strata of mottled sandstone, 400 feet of marl and 335 feet of keuper. If we add to that the Jurassic and Cretaceous deposits of 1,000–1,700 feet, and consider the depth at which the organisms were found in the salt layer, we get a total of about 4,660 feet under which they were buried.

Although they were his own research results, Dombrowski still wondered whether these organisms could really have lived in the Permian seas. "We would then have to assume that they are the oldest type of living creatures which exist in our day, not as the result of a long succession of generations, but as they are, unchanged, with an individual age of 180–200 million years."

Dombrowski's subsequent researches confirmed this. Furthermore, viable bacteria were also found in some salt of Canadian origin which came from a depth of over 3,000 feet and was dated, from its geological stratum, about 380 million years.

In May, 1962, the American Academy of Sciences invited Dr. Dombrowski to lecture in New York, where he announced another sensational discovery. In a salt sample from Irkutsk in Siberia he had discovered two types of micro-organisms aged 650 million years.

Since 1890 there have been at least eight different descriptions in scientific literature of a micro-organism called *Bacillus circulans*, so named because of the habit of its colonies to move rather fast and in circles. A culture can travel round a circle in fifteen minutes. It has been isolated from Permian salts in Germany under strict bacteriological safeguards three times. Dombrowski wrote in the *Zentralblatt für Bakteriologie* that he felt justified in claiming the discovery of a viable *Bacillus circulans* from mineral salts obtained by mining and deep-drilling methods. The "salt strain" isolated in this way is not a primitive stage of today's variant of the bacillus, but a strain possessing more biological capabilities than its modern relatives described since 1890.

The second stage of research on these primeval organisms aims at the problem of their metabolism and chemical structure. As we are able to allow these micro-organisms to continue their normal life, the differences are not likely to be great. On the other hand, it is often possible to draw important conclusions from minute differences. In this case the conclusions will not only concern the micro-organisms and their original live environment, if any, but also geological conditions.

Have these creatures really been "alive" through 380-odd million years? Their age has been established, but the reply to the question of whether they were "alive" during their existence in the salt, without motion or metabolism, must be in the negative.

We return to our starting-point. What is life, and where do we draw the line between living matter and dead? Chemists provide a criterion. "No life without proteins," they say, and the question arises: What had the earth originally to offer for life to start on this basis?

CHAPTER 18

THE OCEAN'S TIDE LINE IN THE LABORATORY

Stanley Miller's amino-acid synthesis. Sugar and sulphur in the age of creation. A dull black slime.

WHEN we ask how life originated on earth we eliminate at the outset one possible solution of the problem, i.e., the possibility that life did not originate on earth but was brought to it from another star, perhaps by meteorites. However, that answer would not take us very far, for we should then have to ask how life arose there. We had better assume that terrestrial life originated on earth.

The land and seas of our planet in its youth were empty and desolate. Sand, rocks and many salts were carried by the rivers into the oceans; earthquakes caused displacement; rivers altered their courses; deep ocean gulfs became shallow lagoons, and finally arid land. In the dried-up areas the hitherto liquid salt solutions crystallised. Cracks filled with water which washed clay particles into them.

Viable forms of life did not arise simultaneously everywhere, even when suitable raw material was available. It is easy to see that only limited areas were at first suitable for life, no matter what its form. A survey of the possibilities eliminates the likelihood that life might have originated on land. In order to produce life, there must not only be the widest possible range of substances to choose from, but they must be close together. A desert wind may perhaps sweep together all sorts of dust particles, but the sea offers much better conditions and ever-changing mixtures. The best environment was undoubtedly the tide line, the boundary between sea and land and air. More favourable conditions could hardly exist elsewhere. The water was full of salts of all kinds, and the land offered large and small crystals of various minerals.

But how did the first organisms containing protein arise?

When a chemist hears of proteins in this context he is inclined to leave the problem alone as too complicated. Protein is not just a mixture of various kinds of amino acids, it is a substance

Bacteria found in a Canadian salt mine at a depth of 3,300 feet. The salt deposit from which the sample was taken is about 380 million years old. (Magnification 3,300)

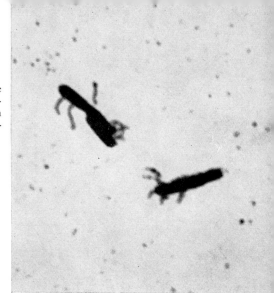

Oil gusher near Bentheim, Emsland, Germany, in August 1957, daily output 140,000 cubic feet of viscous oil. Simultaneous gas eruptions splatter the oil and prevent an even discharge. The water content of the oil fluctuates considerably

The processed skeleton of Oreopithecus. The head is upright. A single tooth lies between head and hand. The nose bridge, which is not ape-like, is clearly visible

in which the constituent amino acids are arranged in a definite order. With infinite care and effort the amino-acid order in the protein of the tobacco mosaic virus, and in the comparatively simple protein-hormone insulin, have been successfully determined, but even insulin cannot yet be produced synthetically. The creation of proteins seemed impossible without the help of a Divine Creator. The amino acids, the "bricks" of the protein structure, are rather delicate organic substances. The idea of finding complicated minerals, i.e., inorganic substances, in their natural state is quite familiar, but although Wöhler caused the assumption of a Life Force to be discarded, and organic compounds, such as are formed in a living cell, can now be made in a test-tube, scientists are still wary of accepting the idea that such substances might have arisen here and there by blind chance. Even if they admit the possibility of their sudden formation, the idea of their getting together and combining to form a living creature appears out of the question to them.

It is easy to see why no scientist was prepared to give his working time to serious experimental research on this matter. Such a study would necessitate a small-scale laboratory repetition of the ocean tide-line conditions. Besides, Nature spent not just weeks and months, but millions of years on this experiment, and carried it out, not in a test-tube but over many thousands of square miles. Even a comparison of the required chemicals would be impossible. In Nature there were seas full of thousands of tons of various salts, and beaches and an atmosphere which contained vast quantities of gas.

It would take exemplary scientific courage, bordering on obsession, to venture on this kind of experiment, for a successful outcome of which there was so little hope.

Stanley Miller's amino-acid synthesis

Nevertheless, there was a scientist who dared undertake the experiment. He started out with the hypothesis that, at the relevant period, the earth's atmosphere contained a surplus of hydrogen. There was also carbon in the form of methane, and nitrogen in the form of ammonia. The oceans covered vast tracts of the earth at that time. Therefore there was water, and clearly the temperature was below boiling point. There were undoubtedly thunderstorms with lightning, i.e., electrical discharges.

Stanley Miller, a twenty-three-year-old student of chemistry in Chicago, followed up the ideas of his professor, Urey, and built suitable laboratory apparatus. He put water into a retort and then injected methane and ammonia. He warmed the contents of the retort by putting a gas flame underneath it, and above this apparatus he built, with two wires, a small spark discharge device, a rather poor substitute for an electric storm.

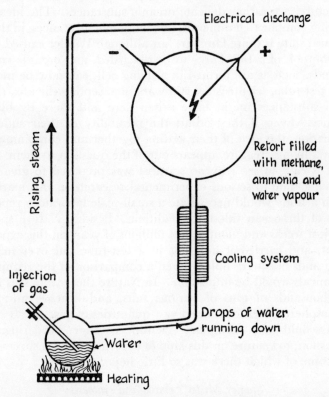

Diagram of the spark equipment as used by S. L. Miller. On the left a retort with water, on the right the spark-discharge device. The closed system contains gaseous ammonia, methane and water vapour

A second glass tube was placed in such a way that any rising vapours were guided back into the retort. The whole apparatus and its contents were kept chemically pure. He started up this rough simulator. Water vapour rose and small sparks appeared. Would anything come of it? Hour after hour passed. They were only hours, however. Miller had no time to wait for thousands of years. Eventually he broke off the experiment.

He analysed the gases in his apparatus. They were still largely composed of methane and ammonia, but there was also some carbon monoxide and nitrogen, just inorganic substances, nothing to shout about. However, they were an indication of what else there might have been on earth during the age when life arose.

Miller then examined the remainder of the substances in his apparatus. The result was startling. There were nineteen different organic substances, six of which were amino acids: glycine, alanine, sarcosine, beta-alanine, alpha-amino butyric acid and N-methyl alanine. All these were amino acids, which are the constituent "bricks" of protein. Moreover, some of these amino acids play a decisive part in the structure of living protein as we know it today. There were also detectable quantities of a number of organic acids which are known to be products of metabolism. The finding of ordinary acids, such as formic acid, would not by itself have been significant, but aspartic, acetic, succinic, lactic and imino-acetic-propionic acids were unexpected. Besides, there was also urea. Altogether 15 per cent of the original methane (CH_4) in the test apparatus had been converted into organic compounds.

A bold supposition had become a fact. The formation of amino acids and other organic substances during the early days of the earth was not only a possibility, but had been confirmed by a practical experiment. It had been a mistake to regard the possibility of amino-acid formation as too unlikely. On the contrary, it would have been a miracle if amino acids had not arisen in large quantities in the primeval environment.

Later Miller simplified his experimental conditions. He left out ammonia and used merely its elementary constituents, nitrogen and hydrogen. He replaced the electric spark by so-called silent electrical discharges, and yet the results remained the same. What was more startling, he need not have bothered to make the experiment. Forty years earlier it had been carried out by Walter Löb, an able German chemist of Bonn, who exposed a mixture of carbon monoxide, ammonia and water to a silent electrical discharge. He, too, obtained traces of amino acids, particularly glycine. Löb's approach had been different; he just wanted to find out what would happen as a result of such an experiment. In his time the world was not yet ready for Miller's train of thought.

Miller's results caused a scientific sensation. A large number of scientists reproduced and confirmed his experiments, and evolved new experiments on the same lines. One problem of interest was whether electrical discharges could be replaced by high-energy light, perhaps in the ultra-violet range. Experiments gave a positive answer to this. The next question was whether radioactive radiation, such as beta-rays, could be used instead of light. Again the answer was that organic substances could be obtained in this way also.

Another scientist took the ultimate step in simplifying this experiment. He wondered whether it might not be enough simply to take an inorganic chemical compound containing all the essential elements and cut out the gases and the water. He chose ammonium carbonate, a colourless, solid, transparent salt which contains nitrogen, oxygen, carbon and hydrogen. He irradiated crystals of this salt with gamma-rays from a radioactive source, and again the result was amino acids: alanine, glycine, ammonium formate and other organic substances.

One may object that, even if amino acids had been formed in this way, they might be immediately transformed further by chemical processes. After all, we have to assume that in a primeval environment amino acids accumulated in large quantities before forming themselves into higher organic-chemical units. However, these doubts were easily dispersed. In analysing fossils, i.e., remnants of ancient animals, such quantities of amino acids were found in samples which were 360 million years old that the acids could be chemically isolated into discrete fractions, e.g., alanine, glycine, etc. Marine sediments found in Texas at a depth of 10,000 feet confirmed these results. They contained alanine, vallene, leucine, glutamic acid, etc. It is an interesting point that these are the same kinds of amino acids as were found in the irradiation experiments. The series depends, incidentally, on the temperatures which the fossilised animals experienced. Obviously the above-mentioned amino acids are durable and can survive, and therefore accumulate. If a period of 360 million years does not seem sufficient geologists can suggest even longer periods. In stones which are 1,400 million years old considerable quantities of amino acids have been found. This allowed conclusions to be drawn about the formation of pre-Cambrian chalk and slate rocks. It was of little importance that the formation of primeval amino acids was slow. They were so stable that considerable quantities could accumulate over a long period.

The following chemical compounds arose, *inter alia*, during the experimental attempts to reconstruct the origin of life from H_2O, CH_4, NH_3 (H_2S, FeS).

Formic acid	H–COOH	⎫
Acetic acid	H_3C–COOH	⎬ Acids
Succinic acid	HOOC–CH_2–CH_2–COOH	⎭

Alanine
$$\begin{matrix} CH_3 \\ | \\ H_2N-CH-COOH \end{matrix}$$

Glycine (glycocoll)
$$\begin{matrix} H_2N-CH_2 \\ | \\ COOH \end{matrix}$$

Amino acids

Alpha-amino butyric acid
$$\begin{matrix} CH_3 \\ | \\ CH_2 \\ | \\ H_2N-CH-COOH \end{matrix}$$

$$O=C\underset{NH_2}{\overset{NH_2}{<}} \qquad S=C\underset{NH_2}{\overset{NH_2}{<}}$$
Urea   Thiourea

⎱ Urea derivatives

$$HN=C\underset{NH_2}{\overset{NH_2}{<}}$$
Guanadine

A non-chemist may see the picture of the formation of complex compounds in experimental conditions more clearly if he bears in mind that the NH_2 base belongs to the amino group and COOH indicates the acid group.

All the above explanations are valid not only for amino acids. A recently published paper showed that various types of sugar carbohydrates could survive many millions of years. In sedimentary rocks 180–300 million years old several chemical sugar types, such as are still found in nature today, could be identified. However these sugars got into the rocks, they certainly survived many geological ages, probably increasing in concentration, and there is nothing to contradict the probability that they were equally stable in the primeval conditions in which life, or at least its chemical preliminaries, came into being.

Incidentally, speculation about the origin of types of sugar by inorganic reactions, i.e., not in plants and animals, is so old that it has recurred in textbooks of organic chemistry for the past fifty years or so. In comparison with proteins, the structure of sugars is chemically fairly simple.

Are amino acids, some sugars and a dozen or so other compounds enough to create a living organism? To answer this question, Miller's experiments had if possible to be extended. Professor Heyns of Hamburg added sulphuretted hydrogen to the original raw materials of Miller's experiments, because this gas, which has a nauseating smell, is supposed to have occurred in the original terrestrial atmosphere, together with an excess of hydrogen. The results were again startling. There was no difficulty in producing an additional group of sulphur-containing compounds, including ammonium thiocyanate, thio-urea and thio-acetamide.

The compounds mentioned earlier consisted of the chemical elements carbon, hydrogen, oxygen and nitrogen, and the later compounds contained sulphur as well. If the composition of the human body is analysed, the predominant element is oxygen. This is not surprising, as our body consists largely of water, a compound eight-ninths of whose weight is due to its oxygen content.

Apart from trace elements, man consists of the following elements, expressed in percentages:

Oxygen	62
Carbon	21
Hydrogen	10
Nitrogen	3
Calcium	1·4
Sulphur	0·64

Sulphur is therefore a rather important element, even if we assume that primeval organisms may have had different percentages of composition. Phosphorus, which will be discussed later, is almost as prevalent as sulphur—0·63 per cent.

A dull black slime

In 1958 Professor Heyns and his colleagues extended their researches a step further. Starting with the assumption that in the upper atmosphere high-energy cosmic rays split water vapour into hydrogen and oxygen, they added small quantities of oxygen to their initial experimental substances. Again they were successful. In addition to other compounds, they obtained guanidine, a particularly reactive organic base.

It would be too much strain on the reader's attention to enumerate all the substances produced by other, similar experiments, of which only one will be mentioned here. J. Oro, of the University of Houston, Texas, showed that Miller's amino-acid synthesis contained hydrogen cyanide (hydrocyanic acid) as an intermediate stage. By basing his further experiments on this ingredient he succeeded, under a plausible imitation of primeval reaction conditions, in synthesing adenine:

$$
\begin{array}{c}
\mathrm{N}{=}\mathrm{C}{-}\mathrm{NH_2} \\
\mathrm{HC} \quad \mathrm{C}{-}\mathrm{N}\overset{\mathrm{H}}{} \\
\quad \quad \quad \geqslant\mathrm{CH} \\
\mathrm{N}{-}\mathrm{C}{-}\mathrm{N}
\end{array}
$$

This is a complex compound, and the possibilities of its generation had been debated for a long time, for it is one of the basic products of metabolism.

In summarising all these research results we see that a few dozen organic compounds originate under primeval conditions much more easily than was formerly believed. The chemist must now ask himself what these compounds would produce if they were to interact, for there is no doubt that they are capable of reacting with each other. What would be the results of such a mixture of substances, plus the water, sand and salts of the primeval world?

The chemist would rightly reply that he had no idea, but it would probably be a dull black slime.

CHAPTER 19

THE AFTERMATH OF CREATION

The origin of oil. The strange metabolism of the sea squirt. Composition of the primeval atmosphere.

... "AND shalt pitch it within and without with pitch", was the instruction Noah received for the building of his gopher-wood ark. The ancient Egyptians were also familiar with the use of pitch for rendering their boats watertight, and asphalt was used as a cement for the building of the Tower of Babel, as well as for building Nineveh. The Babylonians obtained their asphalt from a small lake on whose surface it floated in small and large lumps. When the royal palace in Cairo burned down in 1077, 10,000 jars and 10,000 bottles filled with naphtha (Greek for mineral oil) were lost in the flames. In 1169 Cairo was exposed to the risk of falling into the hands of marauding Crusaders. Consequently 20,000 jars of oil were distributed all over the town and set alight. The conflagration lasted for forty-five days, and nothing but a pile of rubble was left of the town. In ancient Persia there were asphalted roads. The waterproofing of sewage canals with asphalt was first introduced in Babylon. In his work *De re metallica* George Agricola (1490–1555) described how to produce an efficient lubricant for carts by distilling off the volatile constituents of oil.

Asphalt, tar and similar resinous substances have been used from very ancient times as remedies for all kinds of diseases, and not only in Oriental countries. The curative properties of "rock oil" have been known near the Tegernsee in Germany since at least A.D. 1400.

It is not known when the exploitation of the tar pits near Wietze in Hanover started, but Agricola mentions them in 1546. These pits aroused great interest about a hundred years ago when, inspired by a mistaken theory, attempts were made to drill for brown coal below the level of the exhausted tar pits. Drilling, done with primitive oil-well drills, was very difficult. After several layers of sand a trace of oil was discovered at a depth of about 15 feet. At a depth of over 45 feet a small amount of oil was found, together with fine tar-permeated sand. At about 73 feet "much oil" was struck, and further drilling reached new tar layers and released gases.

Professor Hunäus of the then Polytechnical School (now Technical College) in Hanover, who was in charge of the drilling, had finally to stop work at 122 feet after the sum of several hundred "talers" had been spent on this project. On July 1st, 1859, Inspector Hahse, who, on March 6th, 1853, was the first to draw attention to the "oil springs" near Wietze, wrote in his report:

"Further deepening of the bore hole would undoubtedly be of great scientific and technical interest, for a much greater quantity of tar came up from a depth of 122 feet than from 94 feet. It must, therefore, be supposed that the brown coal deposit from which the tar originates lies not much lower down, and the considerable volume of pure tar which has already been reached, and flows readily from the bore hole, would rise in the latter in even greater volume with increasing depth. Such an event would bring unlimited wealth and blessings to the Fatherland and, in particular, to the village of Wietze and to landlord Wallmann, the present owner of the only tar pit still functioning. The famous Wietze tar can at present be obtained in small quantities only, and at high cost, by washing the impoverished surface tar sand with warm water."

The oil yield of July 1st, 1859, was not much, half a bucket in ten hours.

The Chinese are said to have drilled for and obtained oil 1,700 years before the beginning of our era. The great traveller Marco Polo reported in the thirteenth century that much oil was exported in ox skins on camel back from China to Baghdad. Today's oil traffic would be more likely to be in the opposite direction. When Alexander the Great found an oil gusher near the Amu Darya it was considered a good omen.

During the American War of Independence wounded soldiers anointed themselves with oil they found near Oil Creek. They had no idea what power this "sticky stuff" would exert a few scores of years later. Before that Indians had skimmed the seeping oil from the brooks and used it for drinking and anointing. The father of John Rockefeller, the oil king, started his career as a pedlar of oil in the form of embrocations to be used against rheumatism, tuberculosis, cancer and other diseases.

Natural gas played a similar part to tar and oil. It burned for centuries in many places where it escaped from the ground. The Parsees in India were fire worshippers, and erected their temples wherever they found burning gas. Herodotus and Plutarch referred to places where "eternal fires" burned. To-day's ubiquitous motor transport, yes, even our entire civilisation would be impossible without the trinity of tar, oil and gas.

However, it is not for this reason that carbon compounds are discussed here.

The origin of oil

As we have seen, the primary "bricks" of living matter could have been the natural consequence of the fundamental development of the earth. There are arguments both for and against this idea. One of the objections is that if life started in this way by "accident" there must have been many reactive organic substances capable of such development. For every molecule of the primordial life substance there must have been thousands, even millions, of unusable ones. Even in Miller's experiment the number of by-products is considerable. What happened to those thousands of tons of useless matter? Life on earth is not yet so old that such large quantities could have disappeared again in some geological catastrophe. If we consider the Carboniferous period we see that remnants of whatever grew and proliferated then, and subsequently became covered with layers of rock, are still available. We know the type of vegetation of the carboniferous forests and swamps. Palaeontologists have found leaves and trunks of giant horsetails as well as huge trees, and have identified the various plants. Where, then, are the large quantities of carbon compounds left over after the conversion of only a fraction of the available material into life forms? Are there on earth carbon deposits which do not belong to the Carboniferous Age? Certainly there are: oil, natural gas and tar were formed in earlier ages, but this answer still presents difficulties. Some current opinions about the origin of oil are still under discussion, although the fundamental assumptions are accepted.

From the chemical point of view oil consists largely of hydro-carbons with admixtures of oxygen, sulphur and nitrogen compounds. One theory is that oil originated from carbides, but this is untenable. Compounds have been found in oil which are similar to chlorophyll, others are related to haemal substances.

Such compounds, however, are not stable in temperatures above 480° F, and this puts the carbide theory out of court. On the other hand, the very presence of these chlorophyll and haemal types of compounds supports the common textbook view that oil was formed from plants and animals. Even if the details of the process of oil formation are not yet explained, the following is generally assumed to have happened. In bays protected from surf, as well as in current-free depths of the primeval seas, plankton, algae and fish flourished in profusion. For various unknown reasons mass extinction occurred at intervals. The organic substances sank to the bottom, decomposed and were overlaid by new masses of animal corpses and plant débris. Bacteria living in this slime at the bottom of the sea undertook the further transformation of this organic material. In the course of ages geological changes took place; the oil and oily water were forced into other strata, and this explains why oil deposits are found in various geological formations.

This outline of the process is readily comprehensible, and scientists would be happy if they could always find such plausible explanations of natural phenomena.

We shall not attempt to deny that some oil deposits may have originated in this way. The process, however, becomes much more understandable if we also take into account the latest hypotheses concerning the origin of life. Some minor and rather vague indications will then be seen to have gained in importance.

Organic substances originated at the tide-line in incredible multiplicity. They reacted with each other, but in the main they remained inanimate organic substances, although here and there extremely primitive life forms arose. Among them may have been the preliminary stages of the oil bacteria which are still found today.

The strange metabolism of the sea squirt

Some organisms require strange substances for their metabolism, e.g., the metal vanadium. It is possible that this is the explanation of the considerable vanadium content of some types of oil. Venezuelan oil, for instance, contains so much vanadium that two-thirds of its ash consists of vanadium oxide. The Mediterranean tunicates of today may be descendants of the primeval vanadium-metabolism creatures. They are primitive animals and demonstrate clearly what strange forms life takes even nowadays. One group of tunicates, the sea squirts, are colourless organisms, 4–6 inches long, anchored at a depth of 3,300–6,700 feet. Although related to the vertebrates, they produce cellulose in the manner of plants, and build their knobbly shell from it. Apparently they do not even require sunlight for this purpose. When they die, some species of tunicates turn dark blue, because of the decay of their yellowish-green blood corpuscles, which are comparable to our white blood corpuscles. These blood corpuscles contain up to 3 per cent vanadium in a solution similar to haemochrome. Oil also contains considerable amounts of carbon compounds related to haemochrome and chlorophyll.

In order to ingest the vanadium which is essential for their survival, sea squirts possess an absorption mechanism which allows them to abstract the minutest traces of vanadium from the sea-water. This, however, is not their only peculiarity. They also contain more than 10 per cent free sulphuric acid, i.e., they contain more acid than our gastric juice.

Haemochrome and chlorophyll are very similar, except that the former contains iron and the latter magnesium. There are, however, exceptions to this rule. Brachiopods, such as octopuses and squids, contain copper instead of iron. Could this constituent have been vanadium in the case of their primeval forms? We must not be too dogmatic. Even if, at the time of oil formation, there was much carbon monoxide, toxic to *our* kind of life, that should not in itself be an objection to the existence of life in general. The maw worms (*ascaridae*), for example, have a haemochrome which exchanges carbon monoxide for oxygen, and the presence of carbon monoxide in the small intestine of animals, which is their habitat, does not harm them, while for us carbon monoxide is a lethal poison. The multiplicity of possible forms of life and metabolic reactions need no longer surprise us.

Are we justified in regarding oil as the débris left over at the time of the creation of life?

Composition of the primeval atmosphere

Natural gas or methane occurs largely in conjunction with oil. Textbooks treat it as a secondary product of oil formation. Perhaps we can reverse this idea and assume methane to be, at least partially, the residue of the earth's primeval atmosphere. There is another argument in support of this contention.

Natural gas contains up to 10 per cent of helium. We know of no process by which natural gas could have absorbed this rare gas. We therefore assume that helium is also a remnant of the earth's original atmosphere. Nitrogen is also found in natural gas.

There are a few other indications that oil is a product of the period when life originated. At Lacq, in the south of France, natural gas deposits have been tapped which promise a large and profitable sulphur yield. The Lacq gas contains up to 20 per cent sulphuretted hydrogen. There are rumours of natural gas sources containing up to 75 per cent of sulphuretted hydrogen. What is the origin of this gas? Could it too be a residue of the primeval atmosphere? We have already mentioned sulphur bacteria as a primitive form of life. We also know from various data that bacteria of this type have existed for at least 800 million years. It is possible that sulphur, as well as sulphuretted hydrogen, was necessary to the metabolism of these bacteria. The tar sands, spread over an area of 30,000 square miles along the Athabasca River in the northern part of Alberta, Canada, must also be recalled. This deposit is permeated with natural bitumen, a viscous kind of oil, and its industrial product contains 5 per cent sulphur.

What happened to the water of the primeval seas? Sometimes considerable quantities of oily water gush forth together with oil, and this water may be the residue of an ancient sea.

Oil and natural gas apparently contain remnants of the primeval seas and atmosphere. Could oil and gas have resulted from substances which were a useless by-product of the origin of life and thus contain the remnants of primitive living organisms and their metabolic products? Two groups of substances which have not yet been mentioned—sugars and fatty acids—are also contained in oil.

Not only oil and gas provide evidence for the theory of the origin of life and the composition of an original atmosphere, as prerequisites of amino-acid generation. Recent work indicates that there is evidence, incredible as this may seem to chemists, of a primeval period when the main constituent of the terrestrial atmosphere was ammonia. When Miller added ammonia in his early empirical experiments he did it merely because he thought that, if some distant stars have an ammonia atmosphere now the earth might have had it in past ages. Miller was led to this supposition by a number of considerations, but he could not prove it. Even if a remnant of this primeval ammonia was enclosed in a pocket in some rock formation, how could it be found? It could certainly not be found in the form of ammonia (NH_3) after all these millions of years, for ammonia reacts far too easily with other substances. The only place where traces of this ancient atmosphere could possibly be discovered was in primordial bedrock. The proof of the former existence of a terrestrial ammonia atmosphere was obtained by a now somewhat outmoded method of analysing granite. The silicate lattice of its constituent mineral crystals was found to contain free ammonia. Up to 50 per cent of the nitrogen content of granite can be in the form of free NH_3.

The silicate masses of granite absorbed the ammonia of the original atmosphere, and when they solidified they retained part of the gas. The modern development of analytical methods enabled chemists to release the primeval ammonia from its crystal prison and round off our picture of the early days of the earth.

CHAPTER 20

FROM AMINO ACIDS TO PROTEIN

Peptides out of a test-tube. The sphere—a basic shape.
Another artificial primeval ocean. How did the first cells
live? Rejuvenation instead of death.

WE have unconsciously taken a long stride in our pursuit of the development of life. Even after finding out that a certain age in the earth's history apparently favoured the appearance of some constituents of living matter, such as amino acids, we must still remember that this does not mean that complete living cells already existed, possibly in some strange shape. What we call "life" is a sequence of highly complicated chemical reactions.

To return to Miller's experiments. Clarification was still required as to whether there was a possibility of amino acids arranging themselves in chains next to each other, so that protein-type substances could arise. And here the biochemists came up against another difficulty. They knew the exact structure of only a few, relatively simple, proteins, and although they could say approximately which, and how many, amino acids were contained in them, they knew very little about the order in which these amino acids were arranged. Sometimes the structure of one basic protein is built up from several dozen amino-acid units.

On the other hand, we must remember that the production of a chemical chain of amino acids in a laboratory is one thing, while Nature's creation of life is quite another. In the laboratory there are scrupulously clean test-tubes, carefully controlled temperatures and the purest raw materials in measured amounts. Nature, on the other hand, dealt with an indescribable mixture of primeval chemicals whose interactions would have infinite possibilities. There are no limits, therefore, to the wildest speculation, and only an experiment can shed light on the problem. In view of these considerations, scientists very sensibly decided to start on the very simplest elements, and base their tests on the most fundamental assumptions.

Their aim could not be achieved by attempting to reconstruct the inadequately known circumstances existing on earth at the time of the creation of life, but only by a limitation of their experiment to a small number of definite conditions. A few amino acids, obtained in powder form, were put in a test-tube. Nothing happened. They were shaken, mixed and rubbed together, but no reaction took place. The chemists were tempted to add water and form a solution, but doubted the advisability of this. What did the expression "without form and void" in Genesis mean? Did water exist in the age of creation? Perhaps it did, but no one could be certain, so it was better not to try adding water. What other possible factors remained? There must certainly have been changes in temperature; the test-tube was therefore heated. Some amino acids melted, but they still did not react with each other.

This simple attempt to bring about a reaction between amino acids seemed to have failed, but the scientists of the Oceanographic Institute of the University of Florida, headed by Sidney W. Fox, did not give up. They thought that perhaps the composition of the mixture was wrong. All proteins contain a comparatively large number of so-called amino dicarbonic acids. Such acids were added, but still there was no reaction. As a last resort a mixture of various amino acids was poured into a large volume of aspartic and glutamic acid and heated. The mixture melted. It was kept at 330° F for three hours. Whatever the details of the chemical process that went on during these three hours, the final result was that this melt contained a protein-like product.

Again the simplest arrangement of the experiment had yielded results: amino acids plus heat produced protein. Moreover, it was not some uncommon protein, of interest only to a chemist, and not an accidental substance that could be listed as a protein merely by chemical concepts. A nutritive medium was made of the artificially produced protein and a bacillus was injected into it. The bacillus stayed alive in the medium and sustained its life by it, and it grew only a little more slowly than in the medium in which it was usually bred. The artificial substance was "edible" as far as the bacillus was concerned. The chemists had produced a protein which was suitable for sustaining life.

Peptides out of a test-tube

There is one condition in this experiment which might be cavilled at: the very high temperature of 330° F. It is true that

Prof. Joshua Lederberg, an American biologist who, in 1958, received the Nobel Prize for Medicine for his research on viruses and bacteria. He is convinced that extra-terrestrial life exists

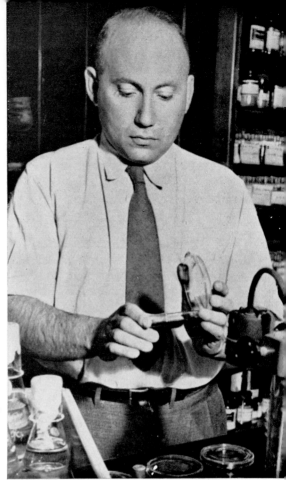

Academician Alexander Ivanovich Oparin of the U.S.S.R. Academy of Sciences whose name is intimately connected with research on primitive life forms. Much of what he published as a hypothesis in 1924 has since been confirmed

"Representation of the awesome vision in the air as seen on August 15th, 1670, in the French province of Touraine." Comets and meteors were always considered as omens of misfortune. For the natural scientist, however, they are merely proofs that creation continues

This is how Johann J. Scheuchzer (1672–1733), a Zurich palaeontologist, imagined the end of the world: the earth is a bursting, flaming globe; below it passes a gigantic comet. Today mankind lives in fear of another, terrestrial, cause of the end of the world: the political misuse of atomic power

such temperatures may have occurred on earth in connection with volcanic eruptions, but they must have been exceptional.

Fox and his team were now faced with the task of finding out whether the same results could be obtained at lower temperatures. In order to improve the interaction of the amino acids, Fox decided to add phosphorus to the mixture.

What had happened before in a tentative and not very satisfactory manner was now repeated without difficulty. In the presence of a poly-phosphoric acid up to 20 per cent of the amino acids combined at temperatures ranging from 158° to 212° F to form a protein-like substance which plays an important part in biological processes.

Again the workers asked themselves whether the protein they had obtained was the right kind of protein. They spent two years examining the products of their experiments. Occasionally the artificial protein looked like a natural protein, and optical tests with infra-red rays proved that it contained "real" protein compounds.

Analysis of their protein yielded the following results: 51 per cent carbon, 4·79 per cent hydrogen and 13·2 per cent nitrogen. The molecular weight was approximately 9,000. A protein of this type can be artificially produced out of eighteen very common amino acids. Its water solubility is the same as that of the known natural protein.

The results of these experiments were so clear and definite that other scientists began to examine the possibility of manufacturing fibres, films and similar products from proteins produced in this manner.

There is only one important difference. An animal organism reacts with shock to an alien protein, and forms antibodies. No such reaction is produced by a synthetic protein, which can be injected into animals without provoking the formation of antibodies.

Fox did not remain the only worker in this field for long. In 1958 another American scientist made an experiment which produced a similar protein in a much simpler and more convincing manner. He chose as his basic material an aqueous solution of ammonium chloride, through which he slowly passed methane. Carbon, nitrogen and hydrogen were therefore present in his experiment, possibly in suitable creative forms, but he was not quite satisfied. He knew that iron was one of the most widely distributed elements in the world, and that

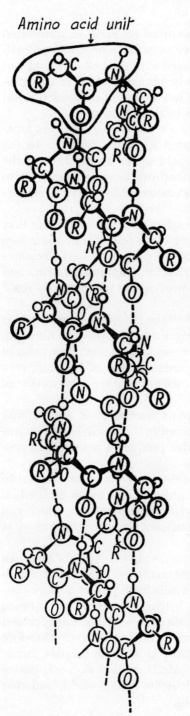

Amino acid unit

sulphur was essential for biological purposes. Therefore he added these two elements to his experimental mixture in the form of ferrous sulphide, a form which he chose after careful thought. As this compound is not soluble in water, he suspended fine ferrous sulphide powder in his mixture, and then exposed the mixture to ultraviolet rays. Only a small quantity of a new substance resulted. Its structural analysis showed that it was similar to peptide, and therefore related to protein. After reduction by customary methods this protein was shown to contain phenyl alanine, methionine and valine.

The sphere—a basic shape

There is nothing to prove that a number of, or even a single, primordial protein was indeed generated in any one of the above-mentioned ways. There is merely a possibility that this could have been the case.

Anyone prepared to accept this possibility lets himself in for

Diagram of the spatial structure of amino acids in a natural protein. The basic part is the left-handed helix formed by a repetition of a CCN group of atoms (carbon–carbon–nitrogen). Other groups of atoms, designated with "R", branch off from the central helix, interlinked with hydrogen atoms (small circles), which loosely connect the nitrogen atoms N to oxygen atoms O, as indicated by dotted lines (according to Pauling)

more than is at first apparent. The proteide, i.e., protein-like substance, that had been formed is a macromolecule, i.e., a complicated atomic structure with certain regularities. Everybody is familiar with macromolecules nowadays. We have them "before our eyes" every day in synthetic fibres and materials. If it is agreed that protein may have originated from inorganic materials (and who would dare to doubt it today?) it must also be admitted that larger and more orderly molecular compounds could have been formed as the result of natural laws operating under primitive conditions. The concept of order, however, introduces the idea of delimitation and spacing, in other words, structure. A structural unit, whether it is a definite sequence of molecules, a side chain, a ring or some similar structure, is discrete and can be distinguished chemically and physically from other structures. In brief, it affects its environment individually.

Returning now to proteins, we note that some of them perform specific functions. How they perform them in each individual case depends on a multiplicity of secondary conditions, such as temperature, reaction medium, etc.

Biochemists could compile long lists detailing the reactivity of various protein substances. Speaking very generally, there is hardly a protein in the human body which does not produce a specific effect, e.g., as a hormone, digestive juice, secretion or other auxiliary substance. There are even reasons to suppose that our memory, and with it our very knowledge, is based on certain protein compounds. It sounds a fantastic idea. When we learn something, new protein compounds are linked together or transposed; when we think, a scanning process examines the structure of some protein macromolecule.

All these considerations have nothing, or little, to do with the outward shape of a living organism. In the experiments imitating the process of the origin of primeval protein, only proteides, but no larger constituent units of living matter, were obtained. Fox wanted to achieve this. Obviously this meant that he would have to expose his mixture to other reaction conditions such as may have existed in the days of creation.

How do proteides react with water? To try an experiment with pure water would be pointless, for chemically pure H_2O was not likely to have existed in those days. A sporadic flooding of land was, however, possible. The addition of sea-water might therefore be well worth trying. Fox added 15 mg of his precious preparation to 3 cc of sea-water and heated the mixture for a minute at 100° C. Chemically speaking, this seemed hopeless, because protein curdles when boiled, i.e., is destroyed. Why should Fox have expected anything else? When the solution cooled down he examined it carefully. It had, indeed, changed, and was now full of minute globules which showed up clearly under the microscope. A certain measure of success had thus been achieved, even if it could be pointed out that the globular is, after all, one of the simplest shapes, if not the most primitive of all. Nevertheless, before this experiment nobody could have predicted whether globules or rods, or indeed a precipitate of any shape at all, would result.

Something important had, indeed, happened. Nothing but globules originated, little spheres of almost equal size. The scientific triumph lay in the demonstration that under suitable conditions primitive protein assumed a uniform shape.

The question arose of what time would do to these globules. Fox left his solution undisturbed for weeks. The globules retained their shape. They did not disintegrate, nor did they change in size. It was even possible to remove the surplus solution by centrifuging without destroying them. It is understandable that Fox classified them as "cell-like". As the globules had the size and some other properties of primitive bacteria, some scientists believed that they could be classed as such.

In further experiments the conditions were varied in many ways, but in nearly every case the result was a globular sediment. If occasionally sickle shapes originated, that particular mixture produced no shapes other than sickles. There was never a mixture of shapes.

Another artificial primeval ocean

Sensational conclusions were drawn by A. T. Wilson from his experiment which at first looked like a Miller experiment. They refer both to the outward form and to the chemical reactivity of the product. Wilson, who works at Victoria University, Wellington, New Zealand, communicated his results in *Nature* in December, 1960. He unhesitantly linked his experiments with the problem of the origin of oil, and went a step further. His "primeval ocean" consisted of 100 cc of water in which he suspended the ash of 10 g of ordinary baker's yeast. As he had calcined the yeast at a temperature of 600° C, it was unlikely that any kind of organic compound was still present. The advantage over earlier experiments lay in the fact that, with the yeast ash, he inadvertently introduced traces of several elements. After adding ammonia and sulphuretted hydrogen to his suspension he poured this "primeval ocean" into a retort, added methane and staged a "thunderstorm" by the impact of electrical sparks.

The first signs of a reaction showed after only an hour; foam formed when the retort was shaken. Four hours later the surface of the water was covered by an insoluble, thin, transparent film. Its analysis showed the presence of carbon, hydrogen and a little nitrogen, as well as a trace of oxygen. Its ignition temperature was 400° C. It was wettable and could be dyed, i.e., it had chemical reactivity. Its rough, foliated structure showed up under an electron microscope. The experiment had produced hydrocarbon macromolecules, i.e., waxes and paraffins, materials which are related to substances found in oil. They also occasionally contained such atoms as nitrogen and oxygen, in which cases their reactivity was higher.

The methane "atmosphere" above the "primeval ocean" in the retort had also changed, and now contained hydrocarbon chain molecules.

It might be suspected that the methane decomposed purely under the influence of the electrical sparks, but Wilson showed that his "primeval ocean" also took part in the reaction, because when he left out the ammonia or sulphuretted hydrogen a different product resulted, a substance which did not take dye and could not be wetted.

The consequences of these experiments cannot at present be estimated. Some of Wilson's conclusions should be treated with caution. He believes that the raindrops of primeval times, falling during electrical discharges through an ammonia–methane atmosphere, may have become coated with a film similar to that obtained by him in his experiments. Such encapsulated drops might then have behaved approximately like primitive cells. As the chemical structure of the drops is on the whole, fairly stable, but nevertheless characterised by reactive groupings on the surface, they may, in Wilson's opinion, have possessed extremely primitive enzyme functions. Wilson then discusses a "hydrocarbon life" which may have been a transition to "protein life", and continues: "It is possible that the earth's oil and shale oil deposits are the residues of the degradation of such a substance." He thus agrees with Kropotkin's view about the origin of oil. This prominent Soviet scientist, who works at the Geological Institute of the Soviet Academy of Sciences, attacked the classical theories of oil generation at a Congress in Moscow in 1957.

Incidentally, Wilson's experiment explains a very strange observation made in 1958. An attempt was being made to analyse a fragment of the so-called Cold Bokkeveldt meteorite, which is a stone meteorite consisting largely of silicates. The customary procedure of boiling the meteorite in hydrogen fluoride was unsuccessful. Even after boiling for 140 hours, virtually nothing of the meteorite had dissolved. It appeared that every small silicate grain of the meteorite was encased in a thin hydrocarbon shell which protected it from the hydrogen fluoride. It seems plausible that these shells originated in the way Wilson's experiment indicated.

How did the first cells live?

A review of the experiments described so far shows us that the difficulties initially expected did not arise. The simulated composition of the primeval sea and atmosphere, as deduced by scientists, together with a supply of external energy, was adequate to produce two groups of complex and reactive organic compounds: amino acids and hydrocarbons. Amino acids led to proteides capable of assuming certain external shapes. Hydrocarbons from the beginning formed films, i.e., flat shapes.

A block diagram would look like this:

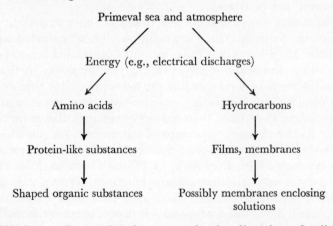

We have advanced quite a way in the direction of cell-like products. We must, however, understand the word "cell" merely in a spatial sense. A living plant or animal cell possesses a multiplicity of characteristics. It is highly organised, has a complicated metabolism and is capable of chemically transforming its contents and of excreting waste material. Initially no biological cell of this description existed. The primitive cell was nothing more than a film-encased blob of matter. It was capable of one life-like function, if it can be so called; it could, within certain limits, absorb food. Perhaps it could be described as a primitive stomach. Its absorption was selective, the "food" being determined by the film enclosing it. Whatever could diffuse and get past the film slipped into the interior, everything else stayed outside. This process was based on the purely physical–chemical laws of diffusion. The primeval cell was incapable of transforming a substance into a suitable food. It could not "digest" anything. Certain environmental substances drifted into the cell, and that was all. Naturally, the cell possessed no enzymes, no heredity protein or any of the other constituents of present-day cells. It had only a characteristic external shape and a primitive inner structure, and this resulted in the concentration of certain compounds at, or near, the outer film surface, or in the centre of the cell. If we want to ascribe an outward "sign of life" to such a cell we can only say that its mere existence created an imbalance in ambient substances, for the concentration of the solution of "eatable" substances surrounding it became weaker.

This thought leads us to the utmost limit of plausible suppositions. Let us once more visualise the possibilities of the corresponding stage of development on earth. The primordial ocean and atmosphere presumably changed gradually. The methane content of the air decreased, and so did the ammonia content. Broad expanses of water became covered with a thin layer of organic material, and more sand and salts were carried into the oceans by the rivers. The earth grew cooler. The cloud cover became less dark, and more ultra-violet rays penetrated to the earth's surface.

These external changes must have given rise to new forms of organic material. Another factor is bound to have had an even more powerful effect: the appearance of oxygen, and the change from a reducing to an oxidising atmosphere.

Wherever thick layers of hydrocarbons covered the water life forms were able to develop which did not need any oxygen, but where oxygen had been dissolved in water countless numbers of new oxygen compounds formed. At this stage anaerobic and aerobic life forms must have differentiated. Such a differentiation is not only possible, but inevitable in our picture of this development. As already mentioned, even now there exist bacteria which can live only when oxygen is excluded from their environment.

The effects of environmental changes are too manifold to survey without further experimental data. This very multiplicity, however, entitles us to assume the generation of new cell systems with more specific and organised functions and properties, and the ultimate development of a large number of cell forms which are more like the cells of today. A singular fact emerges here, however: those cells knew no death.

Rejuvenation instead of death

The question arises whether death existed "in the beginning" or is a phenomenon which arose in the course of development and specialisation. There are arguments in favour of either view. In a previous chapter a tentative statement read that everything living must die. If there is death there must be its residual substance—the corpse. Are we justified in assuming that death has occurred where there is no corpse? There are numerous micro-organisms, unicellular creatures such as bacteria and algae, which grow to a certain size and then divide. Both "children" grow until they in turn divide, and so it goes on. This is real procreation; the old, mature cell has disappeared. Should we use the term "died"? Where is the corpse? There is, incontrovertibly, a kind of life which, according to our concepts, is eternal, is not ended by death but periodically rejuvenated. If we take a piece of tissue of a higher organism, say a mammal, and keep it under suitable conditions it continues to grow and "does not think" of dying.

In 1904, more than fifty years ago, Paul Ehrlich extracted a cancerous growth from a mouse. This cancer has been cultivated ever since, and samples of it have been sent to research workers in many places. Now there is an Ehrlich mouse carcinoma in every cancer research laboratory on earth, where it is bred and used as standard test material for new anti-cancer preparations. Ehrlich's mouse would have died long ago, even without the cancer.

How, then, does sexual reproduction differ from propagation by cell division? Is it simply a similar type of rejuvenation of individuals so highly differentiated that they have special genetic organs, such as seminal and ovary cells? Considered in this way, highly complex animal organisms are just as deathless as algae. What we call their "corpses" are nothing but physiologically used-up auxiliary organs which have to be replaced by new formations so that life may continue. This is a very tempting view, which places our existence in a larger framework, but is rather beyond the scope of our present investigations.

We cannot, however, by-pass the question of the origin of self-reproducing cells. Assuming that the first and most primitive life forms originated because of favourable chemical conditions, each new life form was an individual which started its existence without any reference to, or dependence on, any other life form. Among this multitude of individuals there must have been some which contained chemical compounds which could function as a structural pattern, i.e., these units were capable of building up more of their particular chemical substance from the materials available to the cell. When a complete balance of such an accretion of this substance was reached two identical parts separated from each other. Accretions of chemical compounds have been known for a long time. A form of accretion which must have been of decisive importance during the period when life originated was an accumulation of amino acids on clay minerals. The widely occurring clay mineral vermiculite collects between its layers the following amino acids: beta-alanine, glycine, gamma-amino-butyric acid and ϵ-amino-propionic acid.

This kind of accretion, internal or on the surface, is not limited to simple substances. According to the latest investigations, complex protein compounds, such as are found in highly developed living organisms, are capable of attracting molecules of the same type. Moreover, the accretions are linked so closely with the original molecule that the new structures retain the original spatial arrangement. What astonishes the biochemists most is the fact that this process is possible even without the presence of any auxiliary substance. Thus the original capacity of substances for self-reproduction still exists today, and the chain molecules which originate in this way can be observed through an electron microscope.

There are several reasons why our discussion has been limited to protein as life's cornerstone, as it were. The latest and most topical scientific investigations take place in this field. Plausible theories about the formation of sugars, starch and cellulose have been current for some time. The protein problem is, however, the most difficult and therefore the most interesting.

Scientists who are concerned with the problem of the origin of life can feel satisfied with the results achieved over the past few years. There is every hope that the near future will bring more clues to physiological development.

The fact that many objections are raised against this new trend of thought is stimulating. Such discussions provide ultimately the test of whether all data have been taken into consideration, and whether all the known facts fit together. Thus, the theories of Urey, Fox and others have been criticised on the ground that they provide no explanation for the formation of porphyrines, compounds related to blood and leaf pigments and also found in oil. This objection, however, carries no weight. When we speak of primeval life we must not assume that its forms had already achieved the same differentiated functions as today. On the contrary, we can rightly postulate that it is a characteristic of primitive life that its vital functions were not very specialised. This brings us back to the contemplation of what exactly is to be considered a criterion of living matter. We still do not know when we shall be able to say of the result of a future experiment: This is alive.

There is no doubt that life arose as a consequence of complicated individual chemical reactions which were probable enough in the conditions of the time. We can even go further and say that the very formation of this planet implied that the physical–chemical conditions necessary for the beginning of life and its further course of development were inevitable.

CHAPTER 21

METABOLISM AND LIFE

Liebig examined soldiers. Controversy about yeast. The marshalling yard of metabolism.

METABOLISM must have developed concurrently with changes in environmental conditions. The chemical life processes, as we can observe them today in plants and animals, are very manifold and complicated. We are inclined to believe that changes in their specific manner of chemical transformation hardly ever occur in living creatures. This is by no means so. The submarine atomic-bomb test in the Bikini atoll demonstrated the adaptability of life forms, and the capability of living beings to alter their metabolism.

When research workers began to examine the local plant and animal life for changes some time after the Bikini bomb test they came across some surprises. Various red, green and brown types of marine algae had hardly changed their shape and appearance in the contaminated environment, but their metabolism showed a considerable deviation. In order to continue living, the algae had had to do something about the increased hydrogen peroxide content of the ambient water. Radioactivity had split the water molecules and during this process released hydrogen peroxide, the stuff that we use for gargling, to disinfect a sore throat and kill the bacteria. This toxic substance now appeared not only in the water where the algae lived but also in the algae themselves.

A living organism produces small amounts of an enzyme which can decompose hydrogen peroxide, and the algae had managed to step up the production of this enzyme sufficiently to reduce the hydrogen peroxide to a harmless solution.

This shows that the metabolism of a living organism can react with specific protective measures against a concentration of toxic substances. This happens also on more common occasions during normal life, e.g., during illness.

Minute changes in metabolism, in hormone production for example, may have other consequences, such as the increase in average height of Central Europeans as compared with the previous generation. We are still unable to state the exact reason for this.

Research on metabolism is still in its infancy. Broadly speaking, it concerns the utilisation of food as a source of energy. The organism has to digest the food, and also to form end-products which must be evacuated. The word "metabolism" covers all the hundreds of intermediate stages of this process.

Liebig examined soldiers

If the chemical elements, such as phosphorus, calcium, sodium, iron, etc., which are found by analysis in a living organism were put in glass containers nobody could tell their origin. They do not look any different from the same elements obtained from the soil, or extracted from air or water. There is nothing to show their vegetable or animal origin. The same observation applies to food. Food can be analysed and the result is, as Justus von Liebig indicated when he wrote to his Swedish friend Jöns Jacob Berzelius:

> "I have analysed bread, meat and excrement, and found that a soldier, i.e., a full-grown man (average of 856 men) consumes daily $27\frac{1}{2}$ *Loths* [ancient German measure of weight equivalent to about $\frac{1}{2}$ oz] of carbon, after the excrement had been deducted from the food intake. This amount of carbon leaves the body in the form of carbon dioxide. . . . My work on this subject will run into a small volume."

This volume appeared in 1842, entitled *Organic Chemistry Applied to Physiology and Pathology*. The experimental data which Liebig had accumulated were extraordinarily extensive for his time. He demonstrated clearly that the food intake is "burned" by the body and used as a source of bodily warmth and energy. Waste products leave the body with the breath, in urine, perspiration, etc.

Today we regard these basic nutritive and metabolic processes as common knowledge, but Berzelius, as the then regnant "pope of chemistry", could not agree. He informed Liebig of his objections; Liebig replied with equal firmness.

Friedrich Wöhler tried to mediate between them, and told Liebig frankly: "The manner of your putting forward your controversial opinions to a man like Berzelius, who is also your personal friend, is not at all tactful."

In 1842 open warfare broke out between the former friends about metabolism and its problems. Liebig reported: "Berzelius has broken with me with harsh words by writing me a letter full of insults."

However, their arguments touched only the fringe of the problem, for neither the identification of the chemical elements nor a knowledge of the complicated body mechanism show clearly how food makes the continuation of life possible. How does an organism carry out the chemical transformations essential for its life?

Controversy about yeast

In order to clarify the principle of metabolism as it is understood at present, we shall consider in outline just one section of the total field, i.e., alcoholic fermentation, which became the centre of battle between the warring chemists of the last century.

It was generally accepted that yeast was necessary for fermentation, but this assumption proved false. In the forties of the last century chemists recognised that yeast was an accumulation of certain micro-organisms. It may seem strange to us today, but in that age it had first to be established that yeast did not arise through spontaneous generation. We must remember that a hundred years ago the idea of spontaneous generation still had many adherents. As late as 1888 Ludwig Büchner, physician and writer on natural science, considered spontaneous generation possible, at least for lower organisms. It was Louis Pasteur who succeeded in proving, in face of stubborn opposition, the absurdity of believing in the spontaneous generation of yeast. On the other hand, he still believed that only live yeast could cause fermentation and produce alcohol (plus carbon dioxide). Liebig contradicted him, with his usual forceful vigour.

Both parties collected adherents, and the frontal attacks became more stubborn. Battle cries resounded: "Only live yeast produces alcohol." "Dead yeast does too!" "It can't have been quite dead, some cells must have still been alive!" And so the battle went on.

A chance experiment brought about a solution. In 1896 Eduard Büchner of Tübingen prepared a yeast extract for medical purposes. The yeast cells were crushed by rubbing with sand and the extract separated. There was too much extract to be used up at once, and in order to preserve it, sugar was added, as is usual in households. The result was alcohol.

There could have been no living cell in this extract, and yet it yielded alcohol, a fermentation product. This could mean only that yeast cells are not essential in producing fermentation, but that only one of their constituents is. This constituent was isolated, called "zymase", and the problem appeared solved.

Two years later two facts had been definitely established:

(1) the enzyme "zymase" arises only in living cells, but
(2) zymase can be effective when isolated from a living cell.

In 1907 Büchner received the Nobel Prize for Chemistry for his work and the discovery of fermentation without living cells. He was at that time professor of chemistry at the Agricultural College in Berlin. Ten years later he was killed at Verdun.

For the sake of clarity we repeat the above-mentioned results:

(1) Fruit juice + Yeast = Alcohol
(2) Sugar + Zymase   = Alcohol

The same sort of statement, with slight modifications, was published again in 1944. The picture it presented was a primitive one; it referred to chemical transformation, not metabolism.

The marshalling yard of metabolism

If we today examine the metabolism of a carbohydrate such as sugar we note a number of intermediate stages which finally combine to form a cycle. This is the so-called Krebs cycle, named after Sir Hans Krebs, a German-born biochemist who had to emigrate in 1934 and is now lecturing at Sheffield University. During a lecture he delivered in Stockholm on the occasion of receiving the Nobel Prize in 1953 he displayed a diagram of this cycle. It has been amplified and further developed in the past few years. Hardly anything is now left over from Liebig's early attempts at formulating the process.

We know now of similar cycles affecting the digestion of fats and proteins. There are cross linkages between all these cycles, and if we want to form a picture of the entire metabolism of substances we should get something looking like a marshalling yard. Perhaps the most startling fact is that the various individual cycles which comprise the total metabolic process are absolutely specific. To keep to our simile, a loader at the marshalling yard would not be employed to do the signalling. In the same way each of the many enzymes taking part in metabolism cannot perform the operation of any of the others. And, just as one would not use a shunting locomotive for an

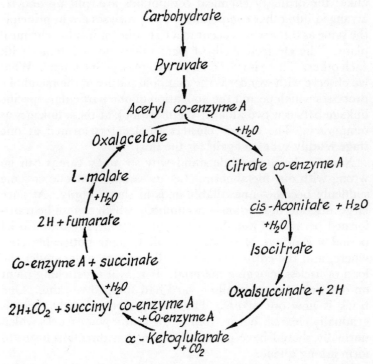

Diagram of the so-called Krebs cycle

express train, so an intermediate product cannot be used until it has been transformed into its usable form.

Almost every day biochemists discover new facts about metabolism. They observe with a sense of wonder how the basic substances of our food, and their various intermediate stages, are transformed step by step into energy with a minimum effort by means of a highly complicated chemical reaction.

Carbon dioxide and water are the end products of this reaction, irrespective of whether we burn fat and sugar in a kitchen range or inside our bodies. The same amount of energy is released either way. By sending it up in flames the process is carried out quickly and brutally, as it were, while the living

223

body operates over numerous intermediate stages, releasing the energy step by step. The body has acquired the art of metabolism and gets its energy through a protracted process which serves its purpose.

In one respect, however, all metabolic transformations are alike: the ordinary chemical compounds are split up and rearranged into other compounds. The processes are in principle the same as those which occur in a test-tube, or in a big chemical plant. The electron shells of elementary atoms interact with each other. There is no secret, no imaginary "life force". What we observe with wonder is the manifold nature of the metabolic processes which permit the activation of one particular, specific linkage between two atoms. We must look at these linkages as temporary. The atomic clusters (molecules) formed at one stage readily split up again for the next.

Now we begin to understand why so many things can go wrong with our metabolism. Let us assume that one enzyme suddenly becomes unavailable or is in short supply. At once large amounts of substances accumulate which cannot be transformed because of the absence of this enzyme. Within a brief period a shortage of substances will become noticeable elsewhere, and the entire organism will begin to suffer under the load of useless, clogging material. It is as if a switching point on one line in a marshalling yard had stopped working. One track is now out of use. The rolling stock already there is gradually cleared, but in front of the faulty point trucks which normally should have passed along in that direction begin to form a long queue.

We have seen, however, that even primitive micro-organisms are capable of adaptation in an emergency. The miraculous cell works not only through the chemical composition of its constituents but also through their spatial arrangement within the cell. Fox's and Wilson's experiments are very enlightening in this respect. We begin to fathom the important part played by the cell structure in the metabolic processes within it. Each internal area of the cell has "a life of its own". In a few years we may know more about this problem, and then we shall realise that what we know today is as inadequate and elementary as the first investigations into sugar metabolism.

CHAPTER 22

LIFE, AND NOT ONLY ON EARTH

Where was the cradle of mankind? 10^{15} "earths" in the universe. Exobiology, a new branch of science. "Organised elements." Microfossils from an unknown world. Other life forms.

WE have been accustomed to regard life as something wonderful and incomprehensible, and the idea of its having begun basically as a logical, and even inevitable, development in the history of the earth therefore comes to us as a shock. Conditions on earth were at one time such that reactions which culminated in the generation of primitive life were inevitable. The expression "culminate" sounds conceited, even if we include man among the life forms. There is no reason for assuming that human life is the peak of development. So far as we can judge, the earth will exist for many more millions of years. There is plenty of time for new, and presumably more highly organised, kinds of life to arise.

The first living organisms appeared on earth about 2,000 million years ago, though there is no full agreement on this approximate date. The oldest animal fossils were found in Australia. They are from 500 to 1,000 million years old and resemble primitive jelly-fish 1 inch long. They may have had a primitive skeleton made of chalk needles. The term "jelly-fish age" appears justified. During the Carboniferous Age, i.e., about 250 million years ago, a profuse amphibian life existed, which was followed subsequently by reptiles, birds, mammals and flowering plants.

When did man appear?

That is a controversial question, all the more so because it is linked with another controversial question: did man descend from apes?

The simplest observations show that, anatomically and physiologically speaking, there are considerable similarities between man and ape. Therefore some apes are grouped as Primates, which term includes, in addition to man, lemurs, baboons, orang-outans, gorillas and, closest to man, chimpanzees. Do these animals descend from one another? The earliest types of primate fossils are about 70 million years old. Where does man come in? Many books, even whole libraries, have been written on the subject.

Let us consider a recent archaeological find. In 1872 Paul Gervais, a French palaeontologist, described the remnants of a lower jaw found in the brown coal pit of Monte Bamboli, north-west of the Massa Maritima in Tuscany. The stratum which contained this fossil was estimated to be 10 million years old. The find was classed at the time as originating from a species related to gorillas, or perhaps baboons. There did not seem to be any close relationship with man.

In 1954, however, doubts began to be expressed. Dr. Hürzeler, of the Natural Science Museum in Basle, decided to check up. He went to Florence, where he heard that in a small brown coal pit at Baccinello, near Grosseto, more finds of *Oreopithecus bambolii* had been made. He called at once on the director of the pit and had it confirmed that many fossilised remains had been noticed, but that so far nobody had shown any interest in them. The coal mine had just been closed down permanently. A search for remains on the ground near the pit during the summer of 1955 proved vain.

By a lucky chance, mining at the pit was resumed in 1956. Some Oreopithecus remains were found among the coal brought to the surface, but they had been almost completely destroyed by mining operations. It was assumed that whole skeletons might still be underground, and the search was extended into the mine proper. New galleries were driven at a depth of 660 feet, but the weight of the mountain overhead was evidently too great for fossil preservation, and no complete skeleton was found. At the end of July, 1958, the excavations were stopped, and Hürzeler was preparing to leave when at last a complete skeleton was discovered. The bones shone ghostly white against the black roof of the gallery. One arm appeared raised, and large groups of bones were visible. Two large blocks of coal were cut out, containing the entire skeleton.

When the bones were extracted and cleaned the creature they belonged to could not be classified. The length of its rump was about 18 inches, and its weight may have been about 100 lb. The arms were relatively long, the leg bones short. The lumbar vertebrae looked strong, a possible indication of an upright stance. The skull was especially interesting. It had a short face, and no "ape-like snout". The nasal roof was clearly discernible, a feature absent in both baboons and man-like apes. The type and arrangement of teeth were studied carefully; they certainly resembled those of early human types. The lower jaw showed a slight projection. Was this the "oldest original man"? Critical studies have since shown that the

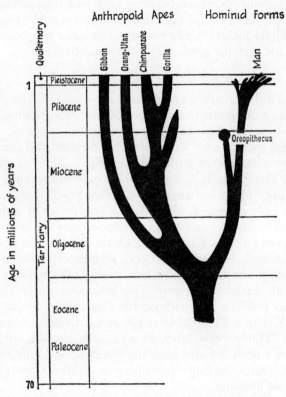

Diagram of man's development. Note the separation of man-like apes from hominids in the Oligozoic Age. Oreopithecus is a branch of the hominids which has come to a dead end. (From Triangel-Sandoz in *Zeitschrift f. med. Wiss.*, 4, No. 5, 1960)

Oreopithecus was not really human, and hardly a direct ancestor of the man of today.

The scientific importance of Oreopithecus is that it may belong to an extinct branch of the development towards man. If this is indeed the case this trend of development must have existed 10 million years ago, long before the orang-outan, gorilla and chimpanzee branched off along their own line of development. In other words, man is not descended from the chimpanzee. If we allow a suitable period for the development of the Oreopithecus line the separation of the ape and man development lines lies 40 million years back.

It would be fortunate if further Oreopithecus skeletons became available. As at least thirty skeletons were destroyed during mining operations between 1956 and 1959 in the Baccinello mine, there is hope that an even better preserved specimen may still be found. Unfortunately the mine has been closed again, this time for good, for it was unprofitable.

Where was the cradle of mankind?

When did a creature appear which we could really describe as human? An increasing number of finds of increasingly older human remains has been made recently in Java, China, Australia, Africa and Europe. The Neanderthal man and Heidelberg man were found in Germany. There is still controversy about details, and the principles of interpreting anatomical similarities are in question. Of *Homo heidelbergensis* we have actually only a lower jawbone which was found at a depth of 80 feet in a sand pit on October 21st, 1907, near a place called Mauer, not far from Heidelberg. During the digging operation the bone broke into two parts and, when treated for preservation later, it was damaged further. Four teeth fell out or broke, and tooth enamel was lost. The bone was put together as neatly as possible, but without the four teeth. It was photographed at an unfavourable angle, and a scientific controversy started. Thirty years later, in 1937, the mislaid teeth were found in a test-tube and carefully inserted, and only then did scientists realise that the Heidelberg man did not lose his teeth during his life-time.

The later fate of this jawbone was no less eventful. After the Second World War it was found by a soldier in the hide-out to which it had been taken for the duration of the war. It was broken again, just as it had been in 1907, and two teeth had disappeared for good.

Nevertheless, anybody who compares the Heidelberg jawbone with that of an ape would immediately agree with the scientists that this is a human bone. There may be more doubt in regard to other finds. How intelligent was this prehistoric man? No animal has ever learned to make a fire, and no animal has systematically manufactured tools. A creature that makes tools should be counted as human, even if his entire work consisted merely of shaping a stone to make it handier, or have a point or cutting edge.

When did the first tool-makers live? The oldest finds of this type are parts of a skeleton of a dwarfish youth, presumably fifteen to eighteen years old, found west of Kilimanjaro in a 500-foot-thick sedimentary stratum. Near the skull lay Stone Age tools, and stones which had been roughly chipped into handy shapes. The age of the find has been estimated at 700,000–800,000 years.

The assumption by Professor Carter, of the Johns Hopkins University in Baltimore, that the first man originated in Africa seems rather rash. However, Carter appears so certain of it that he considers it possible that the descendants of the first human beings in Africa reached the American continent in their wanderings during the Ice Age. The idea that the level of the oceans was lower during the Ice Age, because much water was locked up in the ice, is not new. Perhaps it was really possible during one of those periods to reach Alaska via Siberia. Perhaps this took place 10,400 years ago, in the period for which Libby assumes a spread of population over large areas of North America.

If we wished to give a round figure for the date of the first appearance of man, in our present state of knowledge we should say that man was younger than 1 million years.

10^{15} "earths" in the universe

As long as we were aware only of our own planetary system, and considered the earth to be the centre of the universe, man appeared to be either a miraculous accident or the special work of a creator. Today we know that there are millions of planetary systems, and that our own system is nothing out of the ordinary. Why should man be considered the pinnacle of creation if we know of micro-organisms which have capabilities which we lack, to say nothing of the higher animals, among which there are varieties with finer sense organs, with faster reactions than ours and with better facilities for locomotion?

We must seriously consider the fact that there are more "earths" in the universe, and that there may be life on them, and perhaps beings more intelligent than ourselves.

Before we enter the realm of speculation we must try to define what we mean by "earth" or a terrestrial-type body. If the earth were as small as the moon its gravitational force would not suffice to retain a gaseous atmosphere. Neither would there be water. If, on the other hand, the earth were too big its gravitational force would be so strong that hardly any movement would be possible. This would be a great obstacle to the development of living creatures. An inhabited celestial body must also receive a suitable amount of radiation. Too much or too little heat would preclude life. If the earth were twice as far away from the sun as it is now it would get only one-quarter of its present thermal radiation, and life would freeze to death. Finally, conditions must remain favourable over a considerable period of time; a sudden emergence of life at the time of the formation of the earth is unthinkable.

If we try to arrive at a reasonable estimate of all possible "earths" we have to exclude all planets with basically different physical, atmospheric and chemical conditions. For instance, Mars may be too cold ($+86°$ to $-66°$ F) for life in our sense, to say nothing of its unsuitable atmosphere. Nevertheless, certain seasonal changes in colour on its surface indicate that apparently some organic matter forms there periodically. Venus has temperatures of 554–662° F. There is presumably some water, but only in the form of high-altitude clouds.

Our galaxy, the Milky Way, contains, at a conservative estimate, about $10^{11} = 100,000,000,000$ stars, i.e., suns. Pascual Jordan believes that there are altogether $10^{10} = 10,000,000,000$ galaxies in the universe. If we accept this statement, we have to face a figure of

$$10^{11} \times 10^{10} = 10^{21} = 1,000,000,000,000,000,000,000 \text{ suns.}$$

Certainly some galaxies are not as big as our Milky Way. Therefore we may divide the figure by 100. Of the remaining 10^{19} suns, it is perhaps one in a hundred that has a planetary system. That still leaves us with 10^{17}. The chances are that only one planetary system in a hundred has a planet similar in size and other properties to our earth, i.e.,

$$10^{15} = 1,000,000,000,000,000$$

terrestrial-type planets.

A number of these "earths" would be quite young, too young to have life on them. If we assume, further, that on these "earths" unknown physical conditions prevail which preclude the development of life the fact remains that there must be still many millions of celestial bodies the conditions on which are similar to those existing on our own earth. There could be life as we know it on these other "earths". There may also be other varieties of life and metabolism on other kinds of celestial bodies among the galaxies.

Exobiology, a new branch of science

Professor Joshua Lederberg, a talented young biologist, who lectures at the Stanford School of Medicine in the United States, is one of the scientists who firmly believe in the existence of extra-terrestrial life, and consequently in the need for a new branch of science—exobiology. Lederberg's devotion to science was rewarded in 1958 by the Nobel Prize for his experiments with bacteria and viruses.

"We cannot give a precise definition of life such as may possibly exist on other worlds," he stated. "It would be unwise to exclude the possibility of strange life forms, perhaps in water-less conditions, or without oxygen and at temperatures between 112–482° F."

Lederberg would obviously include life forms which have a vastly different metabolism from our own. Does Lederberg expect to find a kind of life in which silicon takes the place of carbon? In principle such life cannot be excluded, but it would require a long period of development, because of the smaller reactivity of this element. Together with some colleagues, Lederberg has done some preliminary work on an apparatus for investigating life in the universe. He believes that it should be possible to send this device by means of rockets to Mars or Venus, for instance. After landing the device would project a long, sticky tentacle, like the tongue of a chameleon, and collect sand, soil, plants and any micro-organisms that might be present. Small-scale television pictures of the finds could be transmitted to earth.

Latest developments, however, show that we may not have to wait until all the technical conditions for Lederberg's experiment have been achieved. It has been known for more than a hundred years that meteorites sometimes contain organic carbon compounds. In 1857 a stone meteorite fell in Hungary which contained a high-molecular hydrocarbon. We recall here Wilson's experiments, and the meteorite mentioned in that connection. In another meteorite organic material was found which, as analysis showed, consisted of carbon, hydrogen and sulphur, and for which the chemical formula $C_4H_{12}S_5$ was quoted. For the organic material in another meteorite the formula $C_8H_9O_2$ has been cited. These analytical results are rather old. There is no doubt that with more accurate modern methods it would have been possible to recognise a number of well-defined and distinct organic compounds.

The researches of M. Calvin, the Nobel Prize winner, and his colleague S. Vaughan of the United States, show that our hopes are justified. They carefully analysed an iron–magnesium–silicate meteorite which fell in Kentucky in 1950. The constituents were as follows, expressed in percentages:

Carbon	2·07	Copper	0·5
Hydrogen	0·9	Chromium	0·5
Nitrogen	0·08	Magnesium	10·1
Phosphorus	0·02	Calcium	0·5

In addition, there were, *inter alia*, fairly large quantities of phosphorus and iron. The most important result, however, was the isolation of 30 per cent of the hydrocarbons present in the meteorite substance. These proved to possess chains with ten to fifteen carbon atoms. The connection with Wilson's experiments is unmistakable. In addition, the analysis indicated the presence of ring-shaped nitrogenous carbon compounds, and, according to Calvin and Vaughan, these contained cytosine, a substance present in the cell nuclei of living organisms.

In 1908 a meteorite fell in New Zealand, and two of its fragments were found after two days' search. Together they weighed 11 lb. They were not examined closely until 1961, when they were washed in distilled water and their surface ground off to the depth of about $\frac{1}{10}$ inch in order to avoid contamination by any terrestrial substance. Whatever had got into the meteorite fragments during the two days while they lay in the open was thus carefully eliminated. When a powdered sample of the meteorite was mixed with water a light-brown substance, constituting about 2 per cent of the original sample, was extracted. Its exact chemical analysis proved difficult, but it was found to contain a number of organic compounds. Some of them were fluorescent in ultra-violet light, to the chemist a clear proof of their complex structure.

"*Organised elements*"

We shall probably never know where all these meteorites came from, but obviously the conditions at their place of origin were favourable to the generation of preliminary stages of life, unless the meteorites are carriers of remnants of a metabolism similar to that of terrestrial life forms. There was some hope that the tentative conclusions drawn from the investigation of the New Zealand meteorite would be confirmed, but nobody guessed how soon confirmation would come.

On November 18th, 1961, a sensational article appeared in *Nature* by Dr. George Claus, of the New York University Medical Centre, and Professor Bartholomew Nagy, of the Department of Chemistry, Fordham University, New York. In this meticulously prepared scientific contribution, in which there is no superfluous word and every sentence is carefully weighed and considered, the authors thank thirteen other scientists for assistance and advice. Before publication the manuscript was submitted for critical evaluation to six experts in the field, including Professor Urey. Among the scientists quoted as sources are Berzelius and Wöhler. There can be no doubt that the communication was formulated in a manner befitting conclusions destined to serve as a landmark in the history of natural sciences. The first sentences indicate the importance of the work:

> "Microscopic-sized particles, resembling fossil algae, were found to be present in relatively large quantities in the Orgueil and Ivuna carbonaceous meteorites. No such particles were found in two ordinary stone meteorites, namely, in Holbrook and in Bruderheim."

The Orgueil meteorite fell in the south of France in 1864, the Ivuna meteorite fell in Central Africa in 1938. Both contained considerable amounts of water, demonstrably of extra-terrestrial origin. A thin outer crust of heat-fused matter prevented the loss of this water. The interior of the meteorites had never reached a temperature exceeding 390° F.

Claus and Nagy had two samples of the Orgueil meteorite at their disposal, one from the American Museum of Natural History and the other from the National Museum in Washington. The sample of the Ivuna meteorite had also been put at their disposal by the American Museum of Natural History.

Grains of the meteorite samples were crumbled in water or glycerol. The subsequent microscopic examination of all three meteorite samples revealed the presence of particles which were dissimilar in morphology to any known mineral form. The two scientists described these particles as "organised elements", and stated that they resembled, but were not identical with, the morphology of certain species of algae which live in water. These living aquatic algae are capable of producing hydrocarbons comparable with those previously found in the Orgueil meteorite.

The scientists found in 1 mg of the two samples of the Orgueil meteorite 1,650 and 1,700 of these "organised elements" respectively, and in 1 mg of the Ivuna meteorite 1,680 of such particles.

Organism found in the organic-chemical component of the Orgueil meteorite. No forms like this "organised element" have been found so far on earth

Without reservations the two scientists announced: "From these morphological, optical and staining results, we have interpreted the organised elements as possible remnants of organisms."

They described five different forms of organisms of various sizes. Some were small, almost circular, and surrounded by double walls which appeared yellowish-green in transmitted light. The shapes were not completely circular, but had inward protuberances. Some had a surface covered with appendages which, in some cases, appeared to penetrate through the walls. There were also cylindrical shapes with thick walls and finely sculptured wall surfaces. Similar forms are known on earth. However, another form, never before observed on earth, was found in the Orgueil meteorite: a structureless envelope enclosing a central nucleus of apparently hexagonal shape, which may, however, have ten to twelve surfaces. Three of the hexagon surfaces were thicker than the others and served as the bases of three protrusions. The diameter of the entire structure was about 30 microns or $\frac{1}{1000}$ inch.

Microfossils from an unknown world

Although the extraordinary structure of this cell alone proves that these forms come from outside the earth, the scientists adduced further arguments to eliminate any suggestion that their finds might be remnants of terrestrial organisms. They pointed out that particles such as have been found in the Orgueil and Ivuna meteorites could arise only in the presence of plenty of water or moisture. The meteorite samples had, however, been kept in the dry air of museums, and before that had been exposed to weather conditions for only a few hours.

Further, it is important to point out that the Orgueil and the Ivuna meteorites dropped to earth in two climatically quite different areas, and yet contained the same kind of organisms. The Orgueil meteorite landed in a temperate zone, in the south of France, and the Ivuna meteorite, which arrived seventy-four years later, was found in an arid desert region of Central Africa. It is most unlikely that both absorbed a similar type of organism after their arrival on earth. Terrestrial organisms which resemble some of these "organised elements" occur only in lakes or ponds and not on dry land. Besides, there is a great chemical similarity between the two meteorites, which suggests that both are fragments of the same celestial body. It is thus fairly safe to assume that the "organised elements" found by Claus and Nagy are microfossils of organisms which lived on the meteorite, or rather on the celestial body of which the meteorite was part. This proves the existence of life in the universe outside our earth.

Although it may sound incredible, this life is largely similar to terrestrial forms of life and metabolism.

Consequently we have no reason whatever for denying the possibility of the existence of higher forms deep in cosmic space. Man, as observed on our earth, is only a stage of development. There may be earths older than ours, perhaps with conditions more favourable to life and with a more advanced type of "human being".

Other life forms

It may be interesting to speculate about what a higher form of life on a planet older than the earth might look like. Science fiction, to which even serious scientists have contributed in the United States under pen-names, has already made this field its own. In general, one is inclined to be sceptical, or even completely negative about such fictional ideas, but this attitude should not be maintained in all cases.

We are unable to predict accurately for our own earth what things are going to be like in ten, twenty or fifty years. In such a comparatively brief span of time too many minor, special or secondary developments obtrude, so that a view of the future cannot be taken and interpreted properly. To be prophetic, one can only trace known developments back in time and then try to extrapolate the future. This type of statistical exercise is

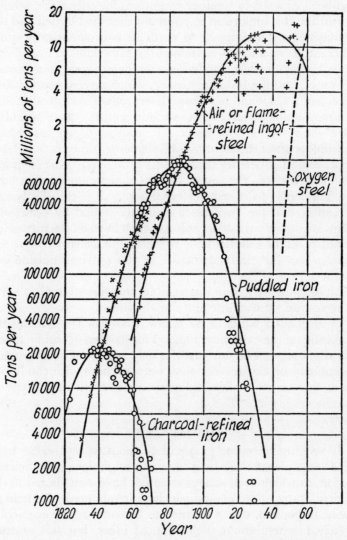

Development of steel production in Rhineland-Westphalia by three different methods during 150 years (Abscissae at equal intervals, ordinate logarithmic). (From K. Daeves and E. Beckel, *Grosszahlmethodik und Häufigkeitsanalyse*, publisher Verlag Chemie, Weinheim, 1958)

possible only when there is an abundance of known data. The principles are simple; we know, for instance, that an industrial process starts on a small scale, but when it has proved its value and caught on the production curve rises until a rival process is discovered.

Karl Daeves, of Düsseldorf, who works on the application of statistical methods in the technical and industrial fields, has published a possible method of determining development tendencies.

In the Rhineland and in Westphalia four methods of steel production were employed between 1820 and the present time. First there was charcoal-refined iron, then puddled iron, later air- or flame-refined ingot steel, and, finally, oxygen steel. If the production figures are suitably arranged they result in three parabolic curves: a steep ascent to a peak followed by a steep drop, the whole curve demonstrating the introduction of a new process, its expansion and its ultimate displacement by a better method. For modern oxygen steels the line is still ascending. Its ultimate bending at the peak still lies in the unknown future, for we are likely to go on refining steel with oxygen for quite a time. There is, however, more to these curves. The ascending curve of the new method cuts almost exactly through the maximum of the old process. Therefore, if the production figures of an older process, in this case a particular type of steel, no longer increase and a new process results in virtually the same output the old process is nearing its end and will soon be superseded. Another prediction can be read from the curves: If the rate of production increase begins to slow down and the parabola is approaching its peak a basically new invention or discovery has been made.

External events, such as wars, can produce small variations in the curves, either upward or downward, without altering their general outline.

It may be possible to superimpose a super-parabola on the individual parabolas. If we had enough data we could predict the total trend of steel production, and see whether steel will retain its importance for long and remain *the* metal of mankind. Even today we can see that plastics are a rival to steel.

Similar development lines can be determined in various scientific fields.

Let us consider the influence of chemistry on our food, clothing and everyday needs in general. Originally man used all his materials in the state in which he found them. Then he became more selective and discovered, for instance, that it was not necessary to eat sugar-cane, but that sugar could be made from it. He began to isolate the substances which were of interest to him, and thus obtained a wide range of materials. This diversification of desired and needed products still goes on. But we no longer just isolate required products from *natural* substances, we have started to build up chemically new substances artificially. Today we still largely use natural substances as raw materials, as they are readily available in convenient form. However, as our demands grow, we find progressively fewer semi-finished products in Nature. We must therefore build up what we require from scratch. Therefore we are finally brought back to the basic substances, such as ammonia, methane, water and air, from which life originated in the first place.

This stage of development is already becoming discernible. Thousands of tons of ammonia products are made from atmospheric nitrogen. Most of them are transformed into fertilisers and used for human consumption in a roundabout way *via* plants and animals. For how long can this go on? Will food based on natural products become an expensive luxury? Chemistry is contributing more and more to our food and clothing; this is a predictable natural development.

The caveman of the Stone Age who chewed raw grains of corn was living in the best possible style for his period. His average expectation of life was pitiably small. Today we live in an unnatural way in many respects, and many an advocate of simple food would like us to return to the eating habits of our ancestors. He forgets to take into account that different demands are put upon us today. Our average age is increasing, and this goes to show how well the "unnatural" manner of life suits us. What is in keeping with one's age is in keeping with Nature as a whole. A way of life which is not contemporary is unnatural; it leads to difficulties, premature wear and tear, and early death. If we view things within this wide framework, predictions for the future become possible.

Attempts at extrapolation in regard to further advances of life, leading to the formation of new species or forms of life, are, however, futile. We have not enough data about past development. This is true of the earth, and therefore even more true in respect of life on other celestial bodies.

Even if we knew the past history of a terrestrial-type planet in every detail we could still not tell how much longer it would take for primitive forms of life to emerge. Even if it already had primitive forms of life, we have no standard of comparison from which to foretell the succession of plants, animals or other organisms. The conditions in outer space are too varied and too unknown. Just as we are unable to make exact predictions over short periods, so we are unable to make them for cosmic eras.

When we encounter "organised elements", such as the Orgueil and Ivuna meteorites brought to earth, we recognise that there is terrestrial-type life in the universe, but we are unable to deduce what forms of life preceded it, or what other forms were contemporaneous with it. The probability estimates of statistics are inapplicable in this case.

Nevertheless, there is an idea, or perhaps we could even call it a law of Nature, which gives us a guiding line for the future. This is the belief in the symmetry of objects and processes, and in the miraculous geometrical order of the world.

CHAPTER 23

THE EVE OF THE SEVENTH DAY OF CREATION

The principle of symmetry in the universe. Creation is still proceeding.

THERE are some who are convinced that the end of our era will also be the end of the earth. This bold assumption is not supported by anything in natural science. We have not the slightest cause for the arbitrary assumption that a creature of our type will be a witness of such a catastrophe. The start of a new age in the development of our planet cannot be predicted either.

Pessimists believe that mankind will one day annihilate itself, perhaps with nuclear bombs. However, it is doubtful whether such a brutal event would be Nature's way of making man disappear. The discovery of nuclear energy was obviously an event marking a stage in man's development, and therefore quite "natural". Why, then, should man perish of it? One might maintain that, thanks to a war-conditioned acceleration of techniques, man laid his hands on the nuclear bomb too early, and not in a logical state of development. But this would require proof that military conflicts are not part of normal development.

It is more likely that mankind will perish through some natural catastrophe. For instance, if the Soviet scientists turn out to be correct in their theory that the saurians died out because of a change in the radiation climate brought about by a nova explosion near the sun, man, being a long-lived animal, would probably likewise be unable to cope with a possible similar change in the radiation climate.

Finally, we must not overlook the fact that there is a "paradisaical" element in the conditions in which man lives on earth among the plants and animals, that an order of things generally friendly to man prevails. We can live only with the help of these plants and animals. We are justified in saying: This animal is like us and therefore eatable, it provides suitable regenerative material for our bodies. This is not surprising, for plants and animals grew up with us on this earth. In other words, all the life forms we know are ultimately based on the same premises, and similar products are bound to result under similar conditions. The individual animal types, however, have different limitations to their life conditions. A change which might hardly affect man directly might, in certain circumstances, destroy our fellow creatures. This might create a situation which would not be amenable to natural regulation and might start a chain reaction of events harmful to us.

The principle of symmetry in the universe

Much of what has been said about our world in previous chapters sounds reasonable and logical. Other things will have to be accepted as working hypotheses to be tested and developed through further experiments, or to be abandoned if found wanting.

Rarely have scientists put forward such bold ideas as they do today. They try to fit together individual facts into comprehensible models of the universe, but this cannot be done without unproved assumptions, and therefore new models proliferate. The preference for one particular model is often a question of taste. Niels Bohr, the famous nuclear physicist, said once that understanding a theory meant getting used to it.

Scientific discoveries not only rouse our doubts about hitherto held opinions, but frighten even physicists or astronomers who are used to handling large-scale concepts. There is, for instance, the spiral nebula, first discovered by radioastronomy and later confirmed by a photograph, which, according to Hubble's law, is 6,000 million light years away. If we accept this figure it means that the nebula *was* in that position 6,000 million years ago. Today it is even farther away.

If we assume, however difficult it is to imagine, that our own galaxy is "at this moment" at the other end of the universe we have to assume fifteen or more thousand million light years as the diameter of the universe. Perhaps we shall be able to understand things better when we know how light units (photons) are changed by their passage through gravitational fields.

Whatever picture of the universe we form, we must start with the axiom that we ourselves are completely unimportant in the processes of the universe. If we are to be objective we must give up any idea that we occupy any privileged position in the universe. Emilio Segrè, the Nobel Prize-winner, summed up the situation in an interview:

> "The principle of symmetry postulates the existence of particles and anti-particles in equal numbers, which signifies equal quantities of matter and anti-matter in the universe. Some of the galaxies which we see in the ultimate distances of the universe may be anti-galaxies, consisting of anti-stars circled by anti-planets. While you and I sit here and talk, there is somewhere an anti-you writing with an anti-pencil, and an anti-me fiddling with an anti-paper knife."

We should not consider Segrè's statement merely as a physicist's contemplation of the problem of matter and anti-matter. It is more than that. It expresses the belief that both worlds are subject to the same kind of natural laws which are the cause of this parallel development. There must be a solar system like ours, and an earth like ours, with a similar geological structure and, according to Segrè's principle of symmetry, with similar events occurring in chronological order.

Creation is still proceeding

Compared with these ideas, proposals and plans for taking up direct radio communications, by means of radioastronomical equipment, with intelligent beings on other planets outside our solar system appear quite modest. Some of these plans, such as those put forward by Edward M. Purcell, a nuclear physicist of Harvard University, have already been put to the test, so far unsuccessfully. Purcell thought that if there were intelligent beings on a certain planet similar to ours at a distance of 10·8 light years they would already have recorded radio signals from us. If they have answered us their code could be discovered. It would be immaterial whether we just recognised a certain rhythm of radio signals, or whether real communication, an exchange of experiences and thoughts, became possible. Even the confirmation of the assumption that somewhere in the universe there were creatures capable of developing a technical civilisation, and of attempting to take up contact over vast distances, would revolutionise our views of the universe. It would never be possible for us to take up physical contact with these beings, and any threatening aggressive attitudes on either side belong to the realm of fiction. No kind of energy discharge is conceivable, and not even a fuel composed half of matter and

242

half of anti-matter could take a space-ship to those regions of the universe in which there is a likelihood of finding life like ours. The best we could ever conceivably achieve would be some kind of television picture. However, lack of direct knowledge does not prevent us from imagining possible civilisations which may be millions of years ahead of us in development. Perhaps they too may be interested in what is happening on earth, or perhaps they have long ago given up looking for life on this planet.

Harold C. Urey said recently:

"I think it possible that intelligent beings on other planets or stars have been sending signals in our direction for millions or hundreds of millions of years, and then simply concluded that there is nobody 'at home' on earth, so they stopped listening and sending."

Much patience is required for seeking contact with other planets. Perhaps we shall have to wait for decades, centuries or even millennia. Should contact be established at some time, involving questions and answers, one generation may be able to put a question and hope that the answer may come across the vast cosmic spaces to the next generation, or even the one after.

This may seem a fantastic idea, but no more incredible than Kepler's and Copernicus's ideas were to their contemporaries. At that time celestial space seemed vast and empty. Today we know that it is by no means empty, but full of huge electrical and magnetic fields of force, cosmic dust, meteors and other matter. We must remember the Van Allen radiation belts which have still to be explored. Concurrently with our "filling in" of cosmic space and increasing our knowledge, new extended relationships were discovered and new ideas developed and verified. If there is any change, it may be simply the greater outspokenness of scientists today, for they need no longer fear being burned at the stake as heretics. Their increased lack of reticence is not due to a desire for notoriety or for airy speculations. They have merely recognised that the world is still full of surprises. They still remain cautious if they write within a framework as wide as that of Sidney W. Fox in his work on the origin of life:

"One can also entertain the idea that life may be starting *now*. Even if all we can safely say is that life had originated at least once, there is increasing reason to believe that life can, nay must, originate over and over again in many places. The existence of plants in many hot springs, and the thoughts of parallel development are in accordance with this idea. The possibility exists that we do not recognise the beginning of new life, because it resembles the undeveloped early forms which are already in existence. Naturally there is no guarantee that life is continuously starting anew on earth at the present time. However, we have less grounds for excluding this possibility than we had before."

This paragraph implies that the existence of plants and animals, which we usually call "life", is a transition stage and not the final form of the total development.

In 1924 the well-known Soviet scientist Alexander Ivanovich Oparin dared to express his ideas about the origin of life on earth. Much of what he postulated then has since been verified. However, it is only now, in the period of the explosive expansion of science, that his ideas have found their way to the west. When his name is mentioned now, everybody knows that the subject under discussion is the origin of life on earth. Few scientists are fortunate enough to have their names linked so closely with such a large field of research. The basic principles of the origin of life on earth are so clear to him that he has already proposed a programme for his future work. He sums up his programme as follows:

"As the forms in which life first appeared during the period in which it generated must have perished at an early stage of development, due to natural selection, and could not have continued to exist in natural conditions up to the present day, we must, in order to draw conclusions about the probable evolutionary process, either complicate artificially created forms by degrees, or examine the fragments obtained from a partial destruction of complete protoplasmic structures."

The immense structure of ideas built up in the Book of Genesis is admirable. It is a concept of the world by man when he still saw himself as the centre of life on earth. Universe and earth, light and dark, water and land, plant and animal are all ordered in a rational sequence. Weighed down with scientific knowledge as we are today, do we really feel it necessary to make essential alterations if we wish to depict the beginning of creation?

If anything has to be added it is only this: The known universe is bigger now, earth and man are unimportant units, we should have more humility and modesty, more gratitude to the Creator who gradually opens our eyes to the greatness of his work, and to the daily continuation of the process of creation which is still proceeding.

"Only a complete fool can be of the opinion that there is nothing to infinite space and the innumerable giant worlds, of which most are probably more favoured than we are, but the light which we receive from them" [wrote Giordano Bruno, the Italian thinker who was far in advance of his time and had to pay for it 400 years ago]. "It is absurd to assume that there are no other living beings, no other thinking capacities, no other senses, than those known to us."

GLOSSARY OF SOME TERMS IN
CHEMISTRY AND PHYSICS

Amino Acids: Chemical compounds which contain an amino group (NH_2) and an acid group (COOH). The NH_2 group generates basic and the COOH group acid reactions. Amino acids are colourless, water-soluble crystalline substances entering into the constitution of peptides.

Aurora: See Northern Lights.

Bacteria: Usually very small, unicellular organisms, either globular, rod-shaped or curved, which cause mould, fermentation or diseases. Bacteria contain no chlorophyll. They obtain their life energy from the decomposition of higher organic compounds, or from the oxidation of inorganic compounds (nitrite, nitrate and sulphur bacteria). Some bacteria types can live without oxygen (anaerobic), some are capable of utilising the nitrogen in the air. The calfactor bacillus can raise the temperature of damp hay to 140° F by the intensity of its metabolism. Many types of bacteria form "spores" when the environment becomes unfavourable, and this enables them to survive droughts, as well as temperatures between + 284° F and − 330° F.

Bohr's Atomic Model: Niels Bohr, 1885–1963, Danish physicist and Nobel Prize winner for Physics in 1922, developed a concept of the structure of the atom which is still sometimes used today as a rough illustration. This is of an atomic nucleus, circled in definite orbits by as many electrons arranged in groups as correspond to the charge in the nucleus. Bohr's atomic model has given the impetus to numerous experiments which resulted in so many refinements that today a comprehensible picture can no longer be presented by a model of this type.

Chlorophyll: A green pigment which occurs in all higher plants. It is chemically related to haemoglobin (*q.v.*), the red blood pigment of animals, but contains magnesium instead of the iron of the blood pigment.

Comets: Celestial bodies which move in sometimes very elongated elliptical orbits in the solar system. Whenever they approach the sun they develop a tail, turned away from the sun and consisting of luminous gas trailing behind, sometimes over several million miles. The head of a comet is comparatively small (a few miles) and consists of frozen matter. Several comets are discovered every year. One of the most famous is the comet whose path was calculated by Edmund Halley (1656–1742).

There is no agreement yet on whether both comets and asteroids originate from a planet which was located in the present position of the asteroids. The disintegration of a comet was observed in the case of the Bielas comet, which broke in two in 1846. Its halves were last observed 1,250,000 miles from each other. Subsequent meteor showers may have been caused by this split.

Cosmic Rays: Also called cosmic radiation, consisting mostly of protons. This radiation was discovered in 1910, but its source in the universe is still not known. It produces in the higher atmosphere of the earth a number of nuclear reactions, the resultant products of which hit the surface of the earth with higher energies than we can achieve in particle accelerators (cyclotrons). Some secondary radiation particles can penetrate more than 300 feet of solid rock.

Counter: See *Radiation Counter.*

Crystals: Solid bodies, the atoms or molecules of which are arranged in a typical geometrical order (crystal lattice). The crystal planes meet at fixed angles. A further law of crystals is the regular repetition of similar planes (symmetry). There are six crystal systems. The simplest crystal shape in the so-called regular system is a cube. The importance of the crystal shape of a substance is clearly demonstrated in carbon; diamond and graphite differ merely in the arrangement of the carbon atoms.

Cyclotron: An installation for imparting high velocities to electrically charged particles. While they are being accelerated the particles are kept on a circular (cyclic) path by strong magnetic forces. Nuclear physicists have made important discoveries about more than twenty elementary particles by means of the cyclotron and its more complex forms, such as the synchrocyclotron, the cosmotron, the bevatron, etc. One of the largest cyclotrons is the proton synchrotron of CERN, the European Nuclear Research Centre near Geneva. Its ring-shaped acceleration path is 665 feet in diameter.

Diaphragm: See *Membranes.*

Elementary Particles: Particles emitted during the physical splitting of atoms. The most important elementary particles are: protons, neutrons and electrons. Some other particles were discovered in cosmic radiation or were produced artificially.

Enzymes: Substances which cause very specific transformations in living cells. In general, they consist of the really active group (co-enzyme) and a protein of very complex construction. When separated, either of these components is ineffective. Sometimes enzymes are called "bio-catalysts".

Erg: Physical measurement unit of work. One erg equals 0·74 times

10^{-7} foot/lb (a million erg equals 0·074 foot/lb). If you climb a flight of stairs you perform work of the order of 30,000 million erg.

Fluorescence: The coloured light emitted by substances when light is shone upon them, even invisible ultra-violet light or X-rays. The colour of the fluorescent light depends on the substance and is almost always of a longer wavelength (i.e., of lesser energy) than the light shining on it (Stokes's law). Fluorescent paint is now frequently used in advertisements to make them show up in glowing colours even in poor light.

Gravity: The force by which two masses attract each other, e.g., the moon and the earth, or man and the earth (weight). This force depends on the mass of the bodies concerned, their distance from each other and the so-called gravitational constant.

Haemoglobin: The red blood pigment, consisting of haem, the red iron-containing pigment proper, and globin, a colourless protein. The structure of globin, which consists of 141 amino acids, was determined in 1961.

Hormones: Organic substances formed inside an organism and having a control function of processes, even when present only in very small quantites. The best-known hormones are insulin, adrenalin and sexual hormones. Frequently hormones interact and exert a most complex control of the organism's functions, e.g., metabolism.

Isotopes: A term introduced by the British scientist Frederick Soddy (1877–1956) to designate atoms of a chemical element which are chemically identical but differ in weight and other physical properties.

Isotope Marking or Labelling Process: Chemical compounds can be labelled by adding either (*a*) radioactive or (*b*) stable isotopes. For example, (*a*) if in a sample of water some hydrogen atoms are replaced by tritium (very heavy hydrogen), the location of this water, e.g., in an animal organism, can be traced by the radioactivity of tritium; (*b*) if some hydrogen atoms are replaced by deuterium (heavy hydrogen) the water can also be traced in an organism by means of suitable measuring devices such as a mass spectrometer.

Magma: Incandescent, liquid, gas-containing molten rock inside the earth's crust. When ejected during volcanic eruptions it appears as lava, which sets on cooling in the form of a porous and vitreous type of rock.

Membranes (Diaphragms): These may consist of a variety of substances. In the functioning of living organisms the membranes of particular importance are those which allow certain substances through in one direction (semi-permeable membranes), thus inducing the concentration of a substance on one side of the membrane. Important scientific and technical knowledge can be expected from research on transport processes taking place in and near membranes.

Meteorites: Meteors which reach the earth from space. They are classed as iron or stone meteorites according to composition. Really large meteorites are rare. Most meteors do not reach the earth. They glow and disappear as they are burned up in the earth's atmosphere (shooting stars). Meteors appear to move in planetary orbits or comet paths round the sun.

Northern Lights (Aurora): A phenomenon which may occasionally be observed in the sky in high geographical latitudes of the northern and southern hemispheres, at an altitude of about 60–600 miles. Sometimes it is a steady luminescence, but frequently there is a display of fluctuating coloured bands and rays. The Northern Lights are caused by the high-altitude collision of electrons with oxygen and nitrogen atoms, and the resultant energy transformations. The earth's magnetic field diverts the electrons, which reach the earth from space, to the poles, and therefore Northern Lights generally appear only in polar regions.

Oxidation: A kind of burning, i.e., absorption of oxygen. However, the decrease of the hydrogen content in a compound is also equivalent to oxidation. In chemistry today any transformation in which a substance loses electrons is called oxidation. (See *Reduction.*)

Peptides: Combinations of amino acids. Two amino acids combining under conditions of water elimination form a dipeptide. Longer amino-acid chains are polypeptides. A typical chemical peptide chain is:

$$\begin{array}{l} R-COOH + H_2N-R \xrightarrow[-H_2O]{} \\ R-CO\text{———}HN-R \\ \qquad\qquad\uparrow \end{array}$$

Peptide-linking of two amino acids

Planets: Satellites of the sun: 1. Mercury, a small planet near the sun, temperature up to 752° F. 2. Venus, nearly as big as the earth, details of surface unknown because of opaque atmosphere. 3. The earth. 4. Mars, tenuous atmosphere, presumably with traces of water vapour and oxygen; variable lighter and darker patches (of vegetation?). 5. Jupiter, biggest planet, about 1,300 times the volume of the earth, but only 300 times the mass of the earth, for it is composed of lighter substances. It has light and dark belts (of atmospheric currents?). The cause of the "red spot" first observed on its surface in 1878 is still unknown. Jupiter's atmosphere contains hydrogen, ammonia and methane. 6. Saturn, similar to Jupiter, has a ring round its equator. 7. Uranus, similar to Jupiter and Saturn, but smaller. 9. Pluto, very small, farthest from sun, little known.

Plankton: Marine plants and animals which drift with the current, as they have little movement of their own, or none at all. Algae, small crustaceans, etc., are part of plankton which serves as food to many marine animals.

Proteins: Albuminous substances which, when decomposed with acids or proteolytic enzymes, result in a mixture of amino acids.

Proteides: Protein-like substances.

Protoplasm: Protein-containing substance in plant and animal cells. It is a liquid and has an optically uniform structure, either granular, fibrous or honeycomb.

Radiation Counter: A thin-walled metal tube filled with gas at a low pressure. In the centre an insulated wire is kept at a higher electrical potential than the tube. If an electron or a gamma-ray enters the tube a brief electrical discharge takes place between the tube and the wire, and this discharge can be recorded. The radiation counter was invented by two German physicists, Hans Geiger (1882–1945) and Walter Müller (born 1905). Today some counters are a fraction of an inch long, others are over 3 feet long. Many types of counters are now manufactured for special purposes.

Reduction: Originally defined in chemistry as the abstraction of oxygen from a compound (e.g., a metal–oxygen compound, i.e., a metal oxide, when reduced, results in metal). The usual definition today is: a chemical process in which electrons are added to an atom (the opposite of oxidation).

Sediments: All rocks erode in time. The débris is washed down by water or carried away by ice and wind, and settles in other places. As this sedimentation is frequently periodic in nature, e.g., seasonal, strata are observable in sedimentary rocks, such as sandstone or slate.

Spectral Analysis: A flame can be coloured by adding certain substances, a fact known and used for centuries in the fireworks industry for producing red, green or yellow lights. If a light results from a mixture of numerous substances it can be split up into separate colours (spectrum) by means of a glass prism. It becomes possible then to determine the kind and quantity of substances which produced the colouring of the light (spectral analysis). In this way we are able to discover from the light of the sun and the stars what substances are present to give the observed colour to the spectrum.

INDEX

255

DATE DUE

SEP 20 '67			
NOV 1 8 '67			
NOV 17 '69			
NOV 26 '69			
F			
FEB 1 '72			
GAYLORD			PRINTED IN U.S.A.